First Published November 2021

ISBN: 9781838388645

Paperback v2

Cover by: doodlescreations.com

Dedication

To my amazing wife and our wonderful
daughters.

Praise for 'The Future of Energy' series.

There are a lot of long, intricate reports, papers, and books about the "energy transition" that are rather dull. This is the opposite. Concise while being comprehensive. Thorough but with a bit of a personal perspective that makes it interesting. Realistic about the challenges but with a dose of optimism about what could be done. Well-informed but accessible. However, the only certainty is that this will change over time so I hope the author can offer regular updates. **David Elmes, Professor, Warwick Business School. (September 2020)**

I'd highly recommend this book to anybody working within energy or interested in learning more about the movement towards clean energy. I'd been looking for a book like this for years but couldn't find anything that wasn't a chunky textbook. This book is both to the point and thorough at the same time. It's very factual and John also offers his expert opinion on particular issues. Looking forward to next edition! **Jon (Amazon, August 2020)**

Great book! Easy to read, informative and concise. Definitely recommend for anyone interested in energy and its future! **Bhavina (Amazon, September 2020)**

Great book by John Armstrong on the future of the energy transition and I recommend it to anybody who has an interest in this field. Having known John for several years he has a great understanding and excellent knowledge around this sector! **K. Singh (Amazon, September 2020)**

The trouble with a lot of experts is they're not so much helping you learn about a subject, they're using you as a platform to either convince people just how clever they are or they're pushing that one silver bullet that will solve their favourite soapbox topic. Not here though, the author takes you on a fairly rapid journey through a range of environmental scenarios (home heating, air travel, industrial consumption) where energy is the problem but also, potentially, brings a range of solutions. Enough detail to keep the purists happy but also simply written so the amateur won't get lost. **Andrew (Amazon May 2020)**

Real world experience makes all the difference. I really enjoyed John's book. What sets it apart is the fact that it is written by someone who's worked in the energy industry. What this means in practical terms is that when the author discusses some of the practical issues, he understands the nuts and bolts of the problems and opportunities. There are plenty of books out there on this subject, but few written with the authority of actual real-world experience. Buy this book. **Mark (Amazon, Oct 2020)**

Contents

The future of energy: hydrogen

Acknowledgements

Thank-you to everyone who read the 'Future of Energy' books and provided such valuable feedback and encouragement.

Foreword

In 2020 I wrote my first book on the future energy system, which I subsequently significantly updated in a new 2021 edition. I found in such a fast-moving topic the best way to keep my thoughts concise and clear was to capture a moment in time and to not be afraid to admit that with things changing so fast the book would need regularly updating to stay current.

The original book covered hydrogen in two chapters, looking firstly at its potential in the energy system and secondly at the potential for ammonia as way of making hydrogen a more flexible fuel. Since publishing the two books the volume of discussion on hydrogen in the media seems to have grown exponentially. Each week governments or companies are making bold statements about hydrogen targets. Despite the regular reporting both the public and the mainstream media seems to remain confused about the technologies supporting a hydrogen system and most importantly about how green these new technologies could be.

In the hydrogen debate I've noticed some extremely polarised views, with proponents extolling it as the answer to all our energy challenges and detractors rubbishing it as an expensive folly. No doubt the truth lies somewhere in between the two. I came to the topic as more of a hydrogen sceptic than supporter and after having researched progress extensively I have emerged still firmly on the fence as to how much hydrogen will or should form part of the energy system. The reality is that hydrogen is already part of the energy system, consuming huge volumes of natural gas in its manufacture already. I believe that decarbonising the hydrogen we currently use extensively in fertiliser manufacture and oil refining is essential in our journey to zero carbon. How much more hydrogen will play a role in the wider energy system very much depends on how it as a technology can compete with others, such as batteries for transport and heat pumps for domestic heating.

As I did in the future of energy books – I intend to delve deeper into hydrogen, unpicking the technologies and asking some open questions.

Hydrogen technology is complex and, in its application, will become interconnected with other technologies across energy systems. It is important to consider hydrogen not as an energy source but a means to transport energy from one place to another. Whereas fossil fuels provide energy themselves, hydrogen rarely appears naturally in its pure form, and instead needs manufacturing from raw materials.

It is a privilege to be able to share with you my thoughts in 'The future of energy: hydrogen'. I don't shy from debate and I'd encourage readers to reach out to me with their thoughts. Every comment is welcomed and acknowledged and contributes towards keeping both this and the future of energy books refreshed and current.

This is very much the 2021 edition of this book. In such a fast-changing field it is going to need regular updates!

IA

$^2S_{1/2}$

H

Hydrogen
1.00794

1s

13.5

1. Introduction

In the future hydrogen may form a significant part of our energy systems. Today it is mostly used in oil refineries and fertiliser but in the future hydrogen could power our cars, heat our homes, and fuel industry. A recent McKinsey study suggested that in less than 25 years, hydrogen could account for 18% of global energy consumption and reduce carbon dioxide emissions from current levels by some 6 gigatons. The impact of such a change in the energy system would be huge, potentially generating $2,500 billion in revenue globally and creating more than 30 million jobs[1].

Given hydrogen's prospects are so grand it is surprising that when surveyed 64% of the general population didn't really know anything about hydrogen technology at all and opinions were largely ambivalent[2]. In another survey, 50% of people had concerns about hydrogen safety[3]. This matters because ambivalence easily turns to distrust. Take for example South Korea where residents protested against hydrogen infrastructure following a fatal explosion at a hydrogen filling station in 2019[4].

The subject of hydrogen is incredibly broad with no simple pathways or solutions. Hydrogen can be made through reformation, electrolysis, or pyrolysis, comes labelled in different colours from simple green to more complicated turquoise, can be stored as a gas, cryogenic liquid, converted to ammonia or even borane and then finally made useful through a fuel cell, engine, or burner. There are countless permutations of how hydrogen can be made, transported, and eventually used all of which will differ in cost, carbon, and risk. It is these that make the topic so confusing and complex. Somehow, the hydrogen story needs to be told so much better to be able to take people with the energy industry through this transition.

In this book I seek to bring some clarity for the everyday reader – to help clear the mist created by these complex and often contradicting terms. Starting by establishing where we are today and looking at the sizeable hydrogen infrastructure already in existence before moving to look at how hydrogen can be made, transported, stored and then finally used across the economy.

I don't seek to advocate any technology, or solution and I don't have a strong view on whether a hydrogen system really is the answer to our search for a lower carbon energy system. Instead, this book seeks to understand an important technology which both investors and policy makers are already steering us towards. With over 448 hydrogen projects already in progress across the globe, and governments such as Japan announcing clear hydrogen strategies[5], this is clearly a technology we all need to take notice of[6].

This book is designed to question, challenge, and raise debate and as such I would welcome your thoughts and comments at the following:

www.johnarmstrong.co.uk/futureofenergy

alternatively, you can email me your thoughts:

futureofenergy@johnarmstrong.co.uk

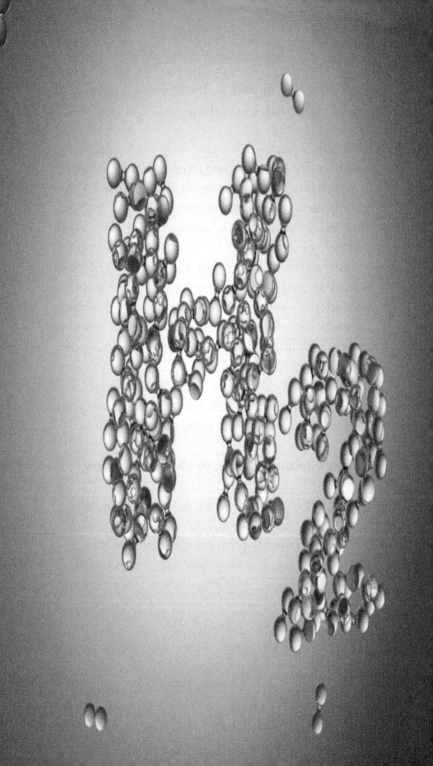

Part 1: Where are we now?

2. Introducing hydrogen

Hydrogen, meaning 'water former', was discovered by Henry Cavendish in 1766. Its name comes from the observation that the by-product of burning hydrogen in air is water[7]. Hydrogen is the most abundant molecule in the universe. In our solar system Jupiter is mostly made up of hydrogen as is the Sun. More locally, here on Earth, most of the hydrogen can be found in water and a small fraction in the air we breathe.

Hydrogen gas is colourless, odourless, non-toxic, has the lowest density of all gases and turns to a liquid at minus 253 degrees Celsius (-434 Fahrenheit). Given the chance hydrogen doesn't want to remain two hydrogen atoms stuck together. It is desperate to react with oxygen in a reaction which releases lots of energy.

Due to its low-density one of hydrogen gas's early uses was in airships – however its ability to explosively react with the oxygen in air caused several disasters, probably the best well known is the Hindenburg airship disaster in which a hydrogen filled airship caught fire in 1937[8].

Today hydrogen is used in large volumes in the manufacture of fertiliser as well as in glassmaking and oil refining. The ability for the world to feed over half of its population is down to the use of hydrogen to make ammonia-based fertilisers, for which one of the main feedstocks is pure hydrogen[9]. Although plants don't use the hydrogen themselves, they are able to absorb nitrogen through the ammonia molecule formed by joining hydrogen and nitrogen.

Hydrogen in its gaseous form also contributes to global warming. It has a global warming potential of 5.8[10] which means that it has 5.8 times more impact on global warming than if the same amount of carbon dioxide gas was released into the atmosphere. For reference the global warming potential of methane gas is much higher at 28 times that of carbon dioxide[11]. Most of us will have made hydrogen in school during science lessons – although we may not remember this now! By inserting two metal bars into a jar of water (a cathode and an anode) and applying a current across the two, hydrogen forms at one and oxygen at the other. Hopefully in science lessons you were then allowed to light each one, to see how the different gases behaved. In each case you may remember inserting a glowing splint in each test tube. The hydrogen makes a satisfying 'pop' whereas the oxygen re-lights the splint. As a gas hydrogen isn't very energy dense with one kilogram of hydrogen occupying eleven meters cubed of space. Hydrogen needs to be compressed or liquified to be able to use it in and meaningful way. As a liquid significant amounts of energy can be stored – however it needs to be cooled right down to minus 253 degrees Celsius (-434 Fahrenheit) to do so – and that takes energy to do. In this form an impressive 71 kilogram of hydrogen occupy each metre cubed.

When we are talking hydrogen in the energy system, we are really talking about hydrogen to transport and store energy. Hydrogen molecules have no carbon in them, unlike other fuels used today. This means that when combusted no harmful carbon dioxide gas is emitted however there may be other emissions such as harmful nitrogen oxides (NOx).

3. Hydrogen use and production today

Global production of hydrogen is currently around 70 million tonnes[12]. That is a big number, in fact it is so big that the current global production of hydrogen is responsible for 2.5% of world carbon dioxide emissions each year. With its 830 million tonnes of emissions annually, hydrogen is already a sizeable contributor to global warming.

Whilst renewable, zero carbon methodologies exist such as electrolysis for making hydrogen, less than 0.1% is currently produced in this way[13]. Most of the hydrogen produced today is from coal and gas through a carbon intensive process called steam reformation. In steam reformation high temperature steam is used to 'blast' apart the hydrocarbon molecules to release hydrogen and large amounts of carbon dioxide.

The 70 million tonnes of hydrogen produced each year is used for two main applications, firstly in producing ammonia for farming and secondly in oil refineries to strip away sulphur from fuel – an environmental measure to improve air quality.

Ammonia production is achieved through the Harber-Bosch process in which hydrogen and nitrogen are reacted together to make ammonia. This is then used primarily in fertiliser (70%)[14], with the remainder being used in chemicals, pharmaceuticals, and refrigerants. Somewhat unambitiously the ammonia industry forecasts making 10% of ammonia from renewable sources by 2030[15]. Globally with increasing populations and demand for food ammonia demand is projected to increase by around 5% a year – and is certainly showing little sign of reducing[16].

Refineries' use hydrogen to remove sulphur from fuels such as diesel[17]. Some of this hydrogen is produced as part of the refining process itself, however over half needs to be produced from processes such as steam reformation of gas. Despite diesel falling out of favour in Europe following various emissions scandals, globally diesel demand continues to grow therefore demand for hydrogen for refining shows little sign of abating[18].

Production of hydrogen from electrolysis (zero carbon) where the electricity is produced from renewables is growing at an impressive rate with annual capacity installed growing by 500% in 2020 vs 2019[19]. With only 0.46mT of hydrogen being produced from renewable sources in 2020 a little over half a percent it will take a huge increase in capacity to decarbonise the hydrogen already being generated.

There is also plenty of experience of storing and distributing hydrogen. In the United States there are 1600 miles of hydrogen pipelines[20] linking both production and underground storage. These supply large hydrogen users like refineries in the Gulf Coast. Where pipelines aren't available, for example, to fuel space shuttles, hydrogen is already distributed in cryogenic liquid form in tankers.

Overall hydrogen technology itself is well developed and mature. Just not in certain applications to enable mass role out of low carbon sources and uses.

4. Public perception of hydrogen

A recent survey in the United Kingdom assessed public perception to be largely ambivalent to hydrogen, with over 64% of participants unable to demonstrate even a basic knowledge of hydrogen technology or its potential to contribute to the energy system[21]. Worryingly one survey found 34% of respondents said that hydrogen was generally dangerous[22].

Public perception matters. Once the public has taken against something it can be very difficult to turn opinion back. Public opinion will influence policy makers and really matters for technologies such as hydrogen to succeed. For a similar example look at nuclear energy's roller coaster journey and continued challenges in achieving growth.

Safety

It probably doesn't help that the first nuclear weapon was called a 'H' or hydrogen bomb, or that in 1936 the Hindenburg air ship's 140,00 meters cubed of hydrogen caught fire. Although these two incidents are a long way away from the way we intend to use hydrogen today – the general public's rare exposure to hydrogen historically has been negative. If you want to worry yourself for a few hours just type 'hydrogen explosion' into google.

Risk perception and tolerance is an incredibly important topic when considering large scale technology change. For hydrogen to work in our decarbonisation journey millions of people will need to embrace new technology. A brief look at other energy technologies such as nuclear and onshore wind demonstrates easily how important the positive engagement of the public is to achieve success.

Carbon

Currently public opinion leans towards hydrogen being environmentally beneficial[23]. Most media articles talk positively about hydrogen's green credentials. In fact, some are overly positive. A good example is a 2020 Forbes article announcing hydrogen as the 'green' fuel of the future[24]. Clearly linking the words green and hydrogen is beneficial in enhancing hydrogen's carbon friendly image but risks oversimplifying a complex topic.

There is a clear risk here that the truth about

current world hydrogen production - which is responsible for 2.5% of global annual carbon dioxide emissions - undermines public trust. It is also a much harder story to tell people that we are going to use 'dirty' hydrogen now whilst the system gets up and running and then switch over later to the green stuff.

Cost

Cost is one of the publics major concerns. A recent UK survey, where respondents were asked about using hydrogen in their homes for heating showed significant objections to hydrogen costing more than they pay now – with 77% unwilling or unable to pay more[25].

Existing fossil fuel and electrical infrastructure has meant that in most countries there is a uniform cost of fuel for transport, electricity, and gas for heating regardless of geographic position. Where significant differences exist between countries, within countries themselves pricing remains largely consistent.

This presents a challenge to any new technology. District heating, where hot water transports heating energy into homes, has been the first 'alternative' to enter the market. Through its 'heat trust' regulator substantial amount of work has been undertaken to demonstrate that costs are comparable[26] to existing technologies. This however has come with significant challenge and examples of negative consumer experiences.

Comparative costs may not be possible with a sustained hydrogen role out. It is however going to be incredibly challenging to convince people to switch if it is more expensive. In a later chapter on heating, I will discuss just how challenging this is and why public engagement really matters.

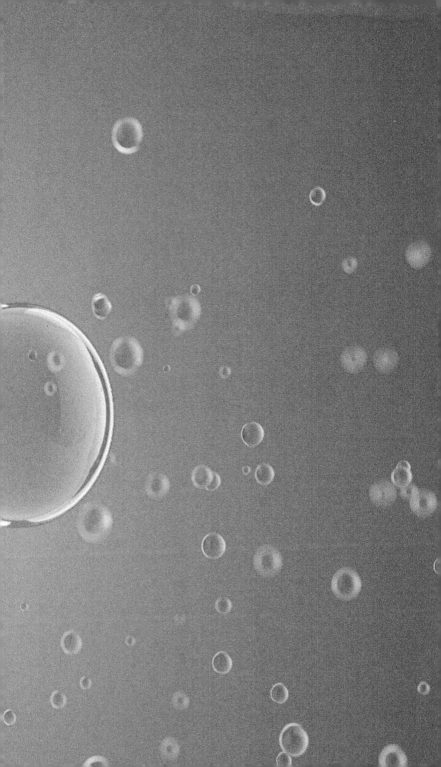

Part 2: Making hydrogen

5. Colours of hydrogen

Hydrogen is the most abundant element in the universe[27]. Here on Earth, it is not found naturally in its pure form and instead is found bonded to other elements, such as oxygen to form water or nitrogen in ammonia. You cannot 'make' hydrogen, you do however need to release it from its chemical bonds so that two hydrogen molecules can stick together into H_2.

Hydrogen at room temperature is a gas and has the lowest density of all gases. This is important when we come to using hydrogen as a fuel which will be covered later in the book.

Hydrogen becomes a liquid at -253 degrees Celsius. This is staggeringly cold and is even colder than the surface of the coldest planet, Uranus, which is a comparatively mild -224 degrees Celsius at its coldest.

When we talk about hydrogen its helpful to label where it comes from. Recently a colour coding has developed for hydrogen using black, blue, grey, and green, however, to make this really confusing there is also yellow, turquoise, pink and even gold! It is a sign of an industry still emerging that the hydrogen colour coding is fluid and regularly mis used.

The following are the current regularly used colour definitions for hydrogen manufacturing technologies:

- **Grey hydrogen:** Hydrogen made from natural gas usually in a process called steam methane reformation (SMR). (For the chemists out there take methane gas, throw some steam at it under high pressure and you get carbon and hydrogen). This is very carbon intensive as energy is used to generate the steam and the process itself releases lots of carbon dioxide.
- **Black hydrogen:** Made from coal (in a process like grey hydrogen) with no carbon capture. Even more carbon intensive than grey hydrogen.
- **Brown hydrogen:** Made from lignite (in a process like grey hydrogen) with no carbon capture. Even more carbon intensive than black and grey hydrogen. Lignite is compressed peat and generates a lot of carbon dioxide when combusted.
- **Blue hydrogen:** Pretty much grey, brown, or black hydrogen but you find a way to store the carbon dioxide deep

underground through carbon capture and storage.

- **Green hydrogen:** Made through electrolysis using renewable electricity to split water into hydrogen and oxygen. Electrolysis works by putting an electric current across two metal surfaces submerged in the water. The oxygen travels to the positively charged 'anode' and the hydrogen travels to the negatively charged 'cathode'. This is easy to replicate at home with a standard battery.

And if that was not confusing enough here are some more[28]:

- Turquoise hydrogen: Produced through methane pyrolysis. In pyrolysis instead of polluting carbon dioxide gas a solid carbon by product is produced. Low carbon.
- Pink hydrogen: Produced like green hydrogen through electrolysis but solely using energy from nuclear power. Zero carbon.
- Yellow hydrogen: Produced like green hydrogen through electrolysis but solely using energy from solar power. Zero carbon.

- **White hydrogen:** Hydrogen made from carbohydrate for example from potatoes or crops.
- **Gold hydrogen:** Naturally occurring hydrogen found in sedimentary rock.

Unpicking the above there are three main ways to make hydrogen. Steam reformation of hydrocarbons, electrolysis and pyrolysis. It is the feedstock of these which changes the colour and influences the carbon intensity. Whilst steam reformation and pyrolysis require a solid fuel like coal, liquid like oil or methane gas, electrolysis requires electricity.

As we have discussed previously hydrogen technologies are already well developed. Currently 95% of global hydrogen is made through steam reformation (black/brown or grey).

Carbon intensity – best to worst

- Green (wind), Yellow (solar), Pink (nuclear) – Less than 0.1Kilogram of Co2 per Kilogram of hydrogen.
- Blue/Turquoise[29]
- Grey [30]
- Black[31]
- Brown - Let's not even talk about using lignite to make hydrogen!

Cost – Lowest to highest

- Black / Brown - $1.2-$2.2/Kg
- Grey - $0.9-$3/Kg[32]
- Turquoise
- Blue - $1.5-$2.9/Kg[33]
- Green - $3-$7.5/Kg
- Yellow/Pink

Gold hydrogen has been left out of the above as its extremely difficult to price or assess carbon intensity of this potential source right now.

Future performance matters

What matters is not the current state but where and how quickly the lower carbon (green, yellow, and blue) technologies can go. Some projections for green hydrogen believe a sub one dollar per kilogram[34] price is achievable through improved and scaled up electrolysis technology and reduced electricity costs. At this kind of price hydrogen would be more than competitive with fossil fuels. Although a reduction of some 80% vs current costs feels exceptional one only must look at the incredible reduction on solar costs (82% over ten years[35]) and offshore wind (66% reduction over ten years[36]) costs to see that reductions in cost which exceed our most extreme expectations are achievable in a ten-year period.

6. Steam methane reformation

Half of the hydrogen used today is made through steam methane reformation (SMR)[37]. The process is quite complex and involves some technical terms such as 'water gas shift' and 'pressure swing absorption'. Putting it simply the feedstock, methane gas, is blasted with extremely hot steam under pressure. This causes the hydrocarbon molecules to split into hydrogen, carbon monoxide, and carbon dioxide.

The key features of this technology are that it emits a lot of carbon in gaseous form and that it uses lots and lots of energy. In addition, a catalyst (a compound to speed up the reaction) is used in the reaction chamber to move it all along.

The 'green' potential for this technology is through carbon capture and storage. By capturing the carbon dioxide, pressurising it and pumping back into old oil reservoirs theoretically zero carbon hydrogen could be achieved.

The potential to capture the carbon released from this process and store it in some form is enticing. The idea and technology have been around for some time with carbon dioxide used to recover more oil from well as far back as the 1970s.

Catching the carbon dioxide before you burn the fuel (pre combustion)

Several technologies exist to capture the carbon dioxide in a chemical process. A good example being in the manufacturing of hydrogen from methane where the hydrogen molecules are split away from the carbon. Once the carbon is removed the hydrogen can be combusted without environmental harm.

Catching the carbon dioxide after burning the fuel (post combustion)

A much-discussed technology for older coal fired power stations was that of capturing the carbon dioxide after combustion. This means keeping the existing technology and installing some 'cleaning' technology on the back end. My favourite description of this is that it is like having an old banger with a shiny exhaust! In this case a chemical solvent (likely amine) is used to absorb the carbon dioxide from the flue gas[38]. By warming and cooling the solvent[39] the carbon dioxide is released in relatively pure gaseous form. It can then be piped to a suitable store.

Transporting carbon dioxide safely

Carbon dioxide can be compressed to near liquid form and pumped safely over long distances. If emissions sources could be linked together then networks could be used to effectively 'reverse' the existing hydrocarbon distribution processes. Existing oil and gas infrastructure could be reversed (with plenty of engineering to make it work) to enable hydrocarbons to become circular with emissions being returned to the beginning of the process.

Safely tucked away deep underground

Porous rock deep underground, potentially in oil reservoirs has the potential to store compressed carbon dioxide gas. Studies have suggested that billions of tonnes of carbon dioxide could be potentially stored in this way[40]. Various studies have been completed to confirm whether the carbon dioxide could be hidden away forever or if all the hard work would be wasted. The technology has the potential to ensure that once compressed and pumped deep underground the carbon dioxide would remain there for 10,000 plus years.

Are negative emissions possible?

Optimistically there is the potential to use this technology to achieve negative emissions. Through capturing carbon dioxide directly from the air, or through burning biomass (trees that have absorbed carbon dioxide as they grow) a carbon negative process could be achieved. Not only could this technology be used to limit emissions from our existing energy use but also from our past. In this case the technology very much exists. What remains is to establish an economic case.

The future

The UK government has set out a plan to remove ten million tonnes of carbon dioxide through carbon capture and storage by 2030[41]. This number sounds impressive until you put it next to the 3400 million tonnes emitted by the UK between now and then and its just 0.29% of total emissions. For carbon, capture and storage to make an impact in overall emissions, goals are going to have to be much more ambitious.

Example project: Equinor Saltend (UK)

The company Equinor has announced a project to build a 600-megawatt steam methane reformer in the UK, linked to a carbon capture system. This project is expected to come online in in 2026[42] with the hydrogen used in local chemical production. Further down the line in 2030 the plan is to use the hydrogen in a power station.

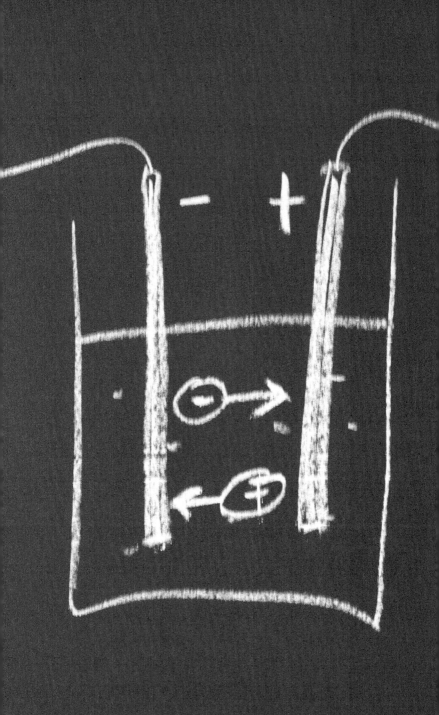

7. Making hydrogen: electrolysis

As a technology electrolysis is clean. You may have seen electrolysis in school science, in which an electric current is passed across a beaker of water – where the positive and negative current enter the water (the cathode & anode) pure hydrogen and oxygen are released. In between both is what is called an electrolyser[43] which is a membrane through which electric charge passes. There is a huge amount of research into making this process work as efficiently as possible through adjusting the electrolyser, cathode, and anode. It takes about five kilowatt hours of electricity to make one kilogram of hydrogen[44]. Industrial scale electrolysis needs a lot of pure water and a lot of electricity. The process produces no carbon emissions, and it is therefore the feedstocks (water and electricity) that determine how green the hydrogen produced is.

Each kilogram of hydrogen gas needs about nine litres of water to produce[45]. It does take 2,400 litres of water to produce a hamburger[46] so in comparison our water consumption to make hydrogen does not feel that water intensive! Water scarcity is however clearly an important consideration if a hydrogen economy were to grow. In countries where fresh water is scarce a switch to a full green hydrogen economy could put strain on already stretched resources – an option may be desalination however this would be even more power intensive.

There are two main types of electrolysis: polymer electrolyte membrane (PEM) and alkaline[47].

Alkaline is the more mature technology and has been used for decades in industry. In alkaline systems the electrodes are suspended in a solution of water mixed with an electrolyte such as potassium hydroxide[48]. The potassium hydroxide is a challenging chemical to handle being corrosive to mist metals[49] which makes the engineering of large alkaline electrolysers extremely challenging. This means that whilst being a mature technology alkaline system have some downsides in being slow to start, requiring stable production, suffering from corrosion, and requiring complicated maintenance[50].

In PEM systems the electrolyte is solid (whereas in alkaline it's a liquid). This removes the corrosion problem and makes the whole system much simpler. This simplicity changes the system significantly, making it easier to stack multiple electrolysers next to each other – meaning that the containerised systems can be literally hitched up to a supply of clean water and electricity and off they go.

PEM systems are quicker to start, don't suffer from corrosion and are simpler and easier to maintain than alkaline ones[51]. Currently it is the manufacturing costs for PEM systems which constrain their use, however as required volumes increase, and technology develops these costs are likely to fall making PEM the dominant technology.

PEM technology is completely game changing for hydrogen as it means that hydrogen could be manufactured at a filling station or even offshore right next to a wind turbine. The 'plug and play' nature of the technology opens huge potential for electrolysis technology and for green hydrogen.

Finally, something that really signals the immaturity of the infrastructure is the current lack of clarity on where is best to do the electrolysis. Should it be done offshore[52] right by the wind turbines and then piped or shipped to shore? Or should it be done where the cables land from the offshore wind farm or should it happen much closer to the point of demand, right at the filling station or near the community being served? Whilst oil and gas have costs and economics which have evolved over decades, establishing the optimum locations for infrastructure development, hydrogen electrolysis remains unclear. As projects develop the true costs and challenges of each methodology will emerge driving this decision and clarifying where it is best for electrolysis to take place.

Example project – Rhineland refinery PEM electrolyser

Shell have installed a ten-megawatt electrolyser at their Rhineland refinery in Germany, using technology from the company ITM. The unit will produce 1300 tonnes of hydrogen a year, using green electricity[53]. The hydrogen will initially be used to reduce the carbon footprint of the refining process. The total published cost of the installation is twenty million euros[54] although this has been subsidised by fifty percent by the EU. This gives an interesting benchmark for electrolysis costs as hydrogen develops.

This is a good example of where the technology can be developed and scaled using the already substantial demand for hydrogen.

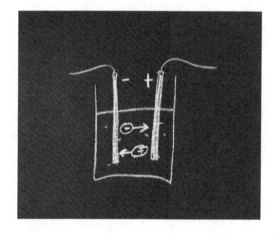

8. Making hydrogen: pyrolysis

Pyrolysis s the process of breaking down chemical compounds at high temperatures in the absence of oxygen[55]. The technology is incredibly exciting for hydrogen. In this case methane gas is split and instead of emitting carbon dioxide gas as the by-product solid carbon is produced[56].

Pyrolysis technology has existed for a while and has often been a technology on the cusp of commercialisation. However, this technology is exciting as the feedstock can be varied significantly. Recent projects[57] have included biomass and waste plastic[58].

There are three main types of pyrolysis technology: plasma, catalytic and thermal.

Plasma pyrolysis is the most mature technology, in which a plasma torch at around two thousand degrees Celsius is used to split methane into its constituent elements. Colder temperatures can be used; however, efficiency drops significantly. Only one site has used this technology in the world opening in 1997, but then closing in 2003[59] due to difficulties making the economics and technology work.

Thermal pyrolysis uses a reactor at a high temperature. This is quite a complicated process and whilst using lower temperatures than plasma should make it easier, the technology is still at laboratory scale only.

In catalytic pyrolysis a catalyst such as nickel is used at temperatures a little below one thousand degrees Celsius. This technology is currently only at pilot plant level.

Pyrolysis technology has one significant downside – and that is the energy used to heat the reactor vessel. Temperatures this high take a lot of energy to generate and currently this is typically achieved with methane. Where feedstock is cheap and plentiful the generated hydrogen can be used – however often this is much too precious to be used for simply firing the furnace. The risk therefore is that turquoise hydrogen is not as green as it could be – particularly whilst hydrogen commands a premium over fossil fuels such as methane.

One area of interest is as a process to dispose of waste. Hard to recycle plastics or tyres for example have the potential to be converted into hydrogen with minimal emissions. Perhaps not the optimum 'circular' economy but better than incineration or landfill. The University of Leeds in the UK is researching technology to heat tyres to around eight hundred degrees and then use a catalytic pyrolysis technology to convert the gas created into hydrogen[60]. Given that there are over 1.5 billion tyres disposed of globally each year – a technology to convert these to hydrogen is certainly an interesting prospect.

Pyrolysis technology remains some way off currently, however, as hydrogen systems develop and demand increases pyrolysis may have a role to play, particularly in managing waste products.

Example project: BASF Ludwigshafen

The chemicals giant BASF is building a methane pyrolysis plant in Germany. Whilst the plant is only at a pilot phase it shows large companies starting to take a serious interest in the technology.

BASF You tube video[61]:

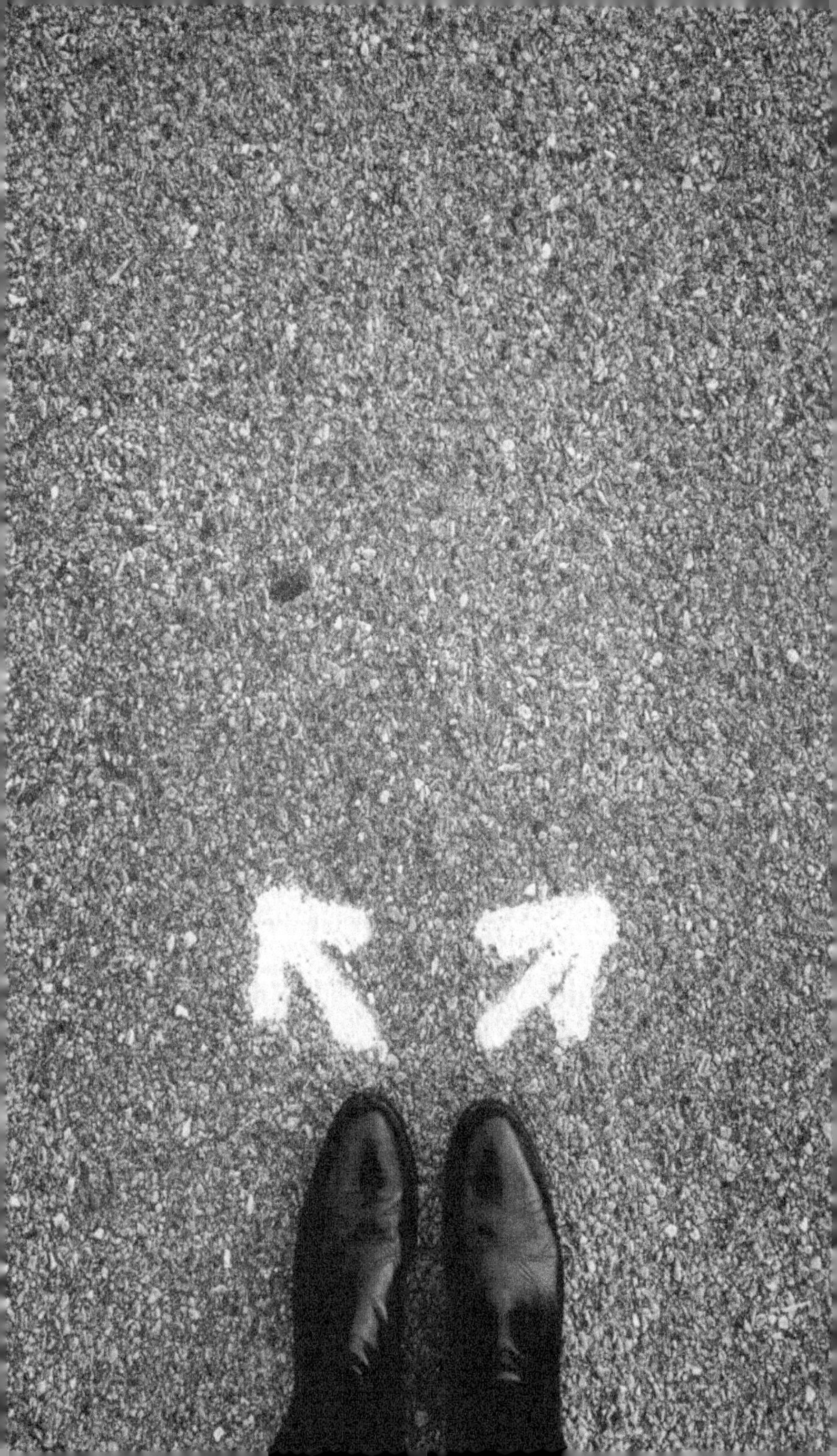

9. Which pathway will win?

It seems that a plethora of technologies exist to produce hydrogen – some green, some not so. Ultimately economics and regulated carbon prices will likely pick the winner. In the event significant volumes of extremely cheap renewable electricity were to become available then electrolysis will win out (so green or pink hydrogen), however large stocks of hydrocarbons remain underground, and it is likely these could be directed towards hydrogen production. If burning natural gas for heating was forced through carbon pricing to become extremely expensive then blue hydrogen could become extremely successful.

A black swan is a technology which is hiding in plain sight – so with hindsight it seems so obvious a change was coming. Pyrolysis feels like the black swan of hydrogen. The ability to process waste, coal, gas, biomass into pure hydrogen and solid carbon if achieved at scale could be game changing for the future of hydrogen.

Part 3: Transporting & storing hydrogen

10. Transporting hydrogen

Making hydrogen is just the tip of the iceberg in terms of engineering challenge. Hydrogen has an exceptionally low energy density at atmospheric pressure. To get the energy density up either the hydrogen gas needs compressing, or it needs liquifying. This presents some interesting engineering challenges.

There is fortunately plenty of experience globally in transporting hydrogen. Already 1600 miles of hydrogen pipelines exist in the United States[62] and hydrogen is regularly moved around in both cryogenic liquid form and as a compressed gas. Additionally, ammonia one of the potential routes for storing hydrogen is already regularly transported as a liquid for use as a fertiliser.

To consider transporting hydrogen in any useful volume we have two main options: compression, and liquefaction.

As with hydrocarbons there are also plenty of risks in moving hydrogen around. A recent hydrogen explosion at a hydrogen vehicle filling station in South Korea highlighted the dangers of hydrogen stored under pressure[63].

Transportation is key to the development of any hydrogen system. Whilst it may be possible to generate some hydrogen close to the consumer, growth will be enabled by the ability to access abundant renewable energy or location with plenty of gas and access to low-cost carbon storage. Both are unlikely to exist right next to centres of demand and therefore transportation will become important in any hydrogen system.

11. Re-using old pipes

Existing gas infrastructure presents a tantalising prospect for enacting a switch-over to hydrogen. In the UK there is already 284,000km of gas pipes in the ground[64] and if these assets could be used, then this could significantly reduce the cost and disruption of a technology switch-over. An interim step could be to blend some hydrogen into the existing flow of methane – we will come to that later.

Firstly, let's rule out using old pipes to move liquid hydrogen. At minus 242 degrees Celsius the energy losses through freezing not just the pipe, but also the ground around it would be incredible. You would also generate a very strange sort of permafrost on the surface above the pipe.

So that leaves us with compressing the hydrogen in a similar way to how methane is piped around now. The existing network is capable of transporting at pressures well over seventy bar (that's high) at a national level, dropping down too much lower pressures (measured in millibar) at a local distribution level.

As a gas hydrogen does have some interesting properties which both help and hinder with this change. In hydrogen's favour is that it compresses easily and doesn't change readily into a liquid – this means it can be piped as a compressed gas easily. Some gases, when decompressed cool to the point of liquifying causing issues further downstream – fortunately, this isn't an issue for hydrogen. Hydrogen isn't corrosive so with the right materials it can be easily transported, and hydrogen isn't toxic – so small leaks won't injure people (provided it doesn't cause an explosion!).

There are however some challenges with hydrogen:

The molecules of hydrogen gas are smaller than all other gases, and it can diffuse through many materials considered airtight or impermeable to other gases.

Hydrogen is explosive across a broad range of concentrations in air[65]. In a lot of cases of methane leakage, we get lucky as methane needs an extremely specific mix with air to ignite. With hydrogen the range of flammable mixes is significantly broader and as such leaks need to be handled very carefully.

Hydrogen is odourless therefore to detect leaks odorant would be required – in a similar way to the addition or mercaptan now in natural gas[66]. Unfortunately, fuel cells have been shown to be sensitive to anything added to pure hydrogen so it may be that odorants for transport need to be removed before final use[67].

Finally, hydrogen contributes towards global warming if released into the atmosphere. Hydrogen has a global warming potential of 5.8[68] which means that it has 5.8 times more impact on global warming than if the same volume of carbon dioxide gas was released into the atmosphere. Although that is significantly lower than the existing methane which has a global warming potential of 28[69]. This means that it is important the system shouldn't be leaky as leaks from the system would have a negative effect on the overall goal of decarbonisation.

Example Project: H21 Project

DNV GL have built a test facility in the UK to see what happens if existing infrastructure is re-purposed for hydrogen. The facility is designed to see what happens if hydrogen is pumped through existing gas pipes right into homes.

The future of energy: hydrogen

12. Transporting via boat

There exists a significant experience in transporting cryogenic (extremely cold) liquids. Liquid natural gas also known as LNG is currently shipped in large volumes at minus 160 degrees Celsius[70]. Ships can carry huge volumes of LNG, for example the 345 metre long 'Mozah' can carry 266,000 metres cubed of liquified methane[71] to LNG terminals around the world. Hydrogen although colder in transit at -253 degrees Celsius could be transported in very much the same kind of way.

There are however some interesting differences – most notably that hydrogen is significantly less dense than methane in liquid form. Methane has an energy density of around 450 kilogram per metre cubed, whereas hydrogen's is only 71 kilograms. This does present an interesting opportunity as the cargo is less dense than water –

liquid hydrogen ships aren't carrying a heavy load and as such can be designed very differently to those in operation today for carrying heavier cargos such as crude oil.

Assuming perfect combustion liquid hydrogen's energy density is around three kilowatt hours per litre compared to LNG's six kilowatt hours per litre. To move the same amount of energy will require either ships twice as large or twice as many ships.

Like LNG ships as the cargo warms some of the precious liquid cargo turns to a gas. This can be used to power the ships engines improving the efficiency of the process.

Moving hydrogen around the world will also take significant investment in supply chain equipment. Hydrogen will need to be stored, loaded, and offloaded all at super cold temperatures. It is not impossible, but it is expensive. Ambient temperatures are constantly pushing against the process and cause the precious liquid cargo to turn into a gas. As with existing LNG infrastructure this is costly, and cargos need moving quickly to destinations to keep costs down.

Example project: Suiso Frontier – World's first liquified hydrogen carrier.

Launched at the end of 2019 the Suiso Frontier transports 1,250 metres cubed of liquid hydrogen at minus 253 degrees Celsius. The ship is designed to show that an international hydrogen supply chain can be established. It is interesting to see Japan taking a lead in establishing global hydrogen infrastructure.

A video of the launch[72]:

13. Blending hydrogen

A transitional step for hydrogen may be to blend it into the existing gas distributed to homes and businesses. Technically this is feasible, and studies have shown that this can be done for up to a 40% blend without having to make significant changes to the existing gas infrastructure[73]. In the UK this has been trialled on a university campus with its own gas grid with a 20% blend[74] and further larger scale trials are planned in the next few years by an organisation called Hydeploy[75]. In the US the HyBlend project is investing fifteen million dollars across a network of laboratories, looking at the implications of hydrogen blending[76].

Prior to increasing hydrogen in the gas system studies need to verify that the following are not unduly impacted by the changed fuel:

- Gas appliances of all ages and types, including boilers, agas, fires, cookers, and

industrial equipment.
- Local gas distribution systems.
- National gas distribution (if hydrogen was to be injected right at the start the supply chain).

Impacts which need to be considered include safety and environmental impact. Local air pollutants like NOx are also hugely important when considering this type of fuel change.

Whilst the Keele study focused on domestic and commercial – industrial users also need considering. Some processes and pieces of industrial equipment are very sensitive to temperature and it may be therefore that hydrogen needs injecting closer to domestic users, to avoid impacting those requiring unblended methane.

Blending may not be the final answer to decarbonisation as hydrogen's potential share seems limited to around the 20% mark - but it is a quick and easy way to take a chunk out of carbon emissions quickly. If green hydrogen were to be used for just 20% of the gas in the UK then this would reduce carbon by six million tonnes, the equivalent of taking 2.5 million cars off the road[77]. This change may be far easier to achieve than other carbon reduction measures – particularly in the next five to ten years.

Example project: Keele University (UK)

A university campus in the UK has run 30 university buildings and 100 homes with a 20% hydrogen mix. The trial was part of a project called Hydeply. The aim of trial was to see how the gas system behaved with a hydrogen mix. The project is now complete, and findings being produced.

A video detailing the project is available here[78]:

14. Storing hydrogen

Hydrogen can be stored as a compressed gas or cooled into liquid form. Both forms come with significant technology, safety, and cost challenges. The safety challenges were highlighted by the explosion of a compressed hydrogen tank in South Korea in 2019 in which several people sadly lost their lives[79].

Whilst it is inevitable in any hydrogen system, liquid and compressed hydrogen will form the main storage techniques – other opportunities exist which through their unique properties may present safer or cheaper alternatives. These typically are split into chemical-based storage where hydrogen is used to create a different chemical, i.e., ammonia or borane or materials-based storage where the hydrogen is contained within a physical material.

Ammonia

Ammonia is the first and most likely choice. Ammonia can be made through reacting hydrogen with nitrogen in something called the 'Harber-Bosch' process. Although the process is quite energy intensive – ammonia does have some benefits which might just make it worth it.

Ammonia is a liquid at only minus thirty-three degrees Celsius[80] (minus 27.4 Fahrenheit). Which is warm compared to the minus 253 Celsius (-423 Fahrenheit) of hydrogen. This makes it much easier to store and transport. Ammonia is also flammable which means it can potentially be used directly as a fuel.

Unfortunately, ammonia is both toxic and explosive. This makes it substantially more dangerous than pure hydrogen. Even small concentrations of ammonia can be deadly and to compound this danger even small amounts released into a confined space are dangerously explosive. That said there is already plenty of experience of handling and using ammonia safely in refrigeration and farming.

Methylcyclohexane (MCH)

The methylcyclohexane process uses toluene as a carrier for hydrogen[81]. To manufacture methylcyclohexane electrolysis is used to bond the hydrogen atoms to toluene. Toluene is a hydrocarbon produced during oil production[82]. The compound produced is a liquid at room temperature and stable for transportation. When hydrogen is required a catalyst is used to release the hydrogen and the toluene can be recycled back to the start of the process. Early experiments have shown a 65% efficiency for the process end to end which may fair well against energy intensive cryogenic processes.

Like ammonia, methylcyclohexane isn't the friendliest of compounds[83]. It is highly flammable and toxic and generally not that easy to handle. That said comparatively to ammonia it's probably preferable and therefore has some real potential as a storage and transporting medium.

Borane

Borane refers to hydrides of boron. Hydrogen atoms love to bond to the element boron. Ammonia borane has been proposed as a stable, nontoxic way of storing hydrogen[84]. Some research exists on borane as a potential storage medium for hydrogen but not too much has happened recently.

Materials based storage

Rather than reacting hydrogen with another chemical another option is to store it in permeable material, a little like a sponge for hydrogen. Suggestions in this space include carbon nanotubes and sticky materials which hold the hydrogen[85].

As more investment goes into hydrogen, I'd expect to see more and more storage propositions emerging. The ability to find safer, cheaper, and easier ways of storing hydrogen could release new applications and although materials-based storage is still in its infancy it's an area to watch.

The future of energy: hydrogen

15. Geological storage

Energy used in heating has a big challenge. When we need it, we need lots and when we don't, we use very little. In the UK the difference between winter peak and summer low monthly usage is pretty much double (around ten billion cubic meters in February vs five billion in August). The within day extremities are even more pronounced. This is particularly relevant for countries with extreme winters where outside temperatures can plunge, pushing demand to extremes. Any system to supply energy for heating needs to be able to manage these extremes and keep people warm and cosy. For most of us we probably take little interest in where the methane gas we burn in our homes is stored. We may see the now disused gas holders as we drive around[86] but other than that gas storage isn't that obvious. There is however a significant amount of storage beneath our feet, where compressed gas is pumped into caverns underground to be retrieved later when required. At times during the last winter 61% of UK gas demand was being met by gas from underground storage[87].

A hydrogen system, with a lot of hydrogen used for heating will need inter-seasonal storage and underground options like that used for methane currently is most likely.

Geologically hydrogen can be stored in various formations. Solution mined salt caverns are one of the most likely contenders as well as depleted hydrocarbon reserves where the removed methane leaves an opportunity to 'inject' hydrogen[88]. There is huge global potential for hydrogen storage, for example in North America[89] where it is believed salt caverns could store a significant volume of the hydrogen, enough to manage inter seasonal variability.

Example Project: Air Liquide Texas

The world's largest underground storage of hydrogen is in Beaumont, Texas, operated by Air Liquide[90]. The cavern is a giant sphere 69 metres in diameter, 1.5 kilometres below the surface. Currently hydrogen from steam methane reformation is stored in it (grey hydrogen) so it's not very green. It does show that hydrogen can be stored in large quantities deep underground. As a liquid 71 kilograms of hydrogen can be stored per cubic metre therefore in this cavern, if full nearly 7000 tonnes of hydrogen can be stored. This is a staggering amount of energy[91].

Part 4: Using hydrogen

16. Converting hydrogen into useful energy

Having gone to a lot of trouble to make, store and transport the hydrogen it then needs converting back into useful energy. The easiest route it to burn it – however hydrogen's properties present some alternatives such as fuel cells.

Combustion engines & gas turbines

Firstly, hydrogen can be burned in air. Burning hydrogen simply creates water. It does however have some interesting properties.

- It is flammable when mixed with either a lot or a little oxygen[92].
- It burns hot and fast. This means that harmful emissions like NOx need to be carefully controlled.

Hydrogen works well in internal combustion engines as well as in gas turbines[93]. Although the comparative energy density, one third of methane[94], means that to generate the same output either the engines need to run at higher pressures or higher flows – put simply to get the same bang you need to push three times as much hydrogen through the engine as you would if it ran on methane.

Fuel cells

Fuel cells work almost like electrolysis in reverse. Oxygen and hydrogen placed separately with a membrane in between along with a cathode and anode produces electricity – typically at about 60% efficiency[95]. With a fuel cell the only outputs are water, electricity, and heat. Potentially therefore in a hydrogen system fuel cells could be used to power and heat buildings or to power vehicles.

Fuel cells vs combustion engines

These two technologies could not be more different. Developments with hydrogen in automotive have typically involved using a hydrogen fuel cell to power an electric motor whereas in domestic dwellings where much more heat is required combustion technologies may be more useful.

Combustion technologies still emit oxides of nitrogen (NOx) causing local air pollution. The flame needs to be carefully controlled to prevent these getting too high. NOx can be removed with a catalytic converter although this adds to the cost[96]. Fuel cells however do not have that challenge.

Overall fuel cells have been shown to be more efficient than internal combustion engines[97]. This of course depends on there being a use for both the heat and electricity. For applications where only heat is required then combustion makes much more sense.

Fuel cells also present an opportunity to combine both hydrogen and battery technology. Vehicles could charge their batteries overnight from the grid and then use hydrogen to boost range or power.

17. Hydrogen in transport

Transport is responsible for 21% of total emissions[98], therefore finding zero or low carbon options for all forms is incredibly important to achieve carbon reduction goals.

Hydrogen has been proposed as an alternative fuel for transport for a long time. The 'Electrovan' from General Motors is considered the first attempt at a hydrogen vehicle back in 1966[99].

Hydrogen in transport can be used in two ways – one is through a combustion engine and the other is through a fuel cell. Whilst a combustion engine will work in a very similar way to a petrol or diesel car now, a fuel cell converts the hydrogen into electricity and water. The electricity is then used to drive an electric motor, potentially combined with a battery.

Hydrogen can also be converted into liquid 'synthetic' fuels and I will cover this in a later chapter.

Hydrogen passenger cars (45.1% of transport emissions[100])

There are an estimated 1.4 billion cars on the road globally[101], with around 64 million sold each year[102]. Currently only a few thousand are run on hydrogen[103]. Hydrogen's main competitor the 'electric vehicle' has sales which are exponentially rising - with the number sold globally expected to be more than 12.5 million by 2025[104]. Hydrogen has a long way to go to catch up.

Hydrogen's unique selling point over an electric vehicle is vehicle range. 'Range anxiety' is the concern that a vehicle won't be able to get to a destination and is the biggest turn-off for people switching to electric vehicles[105].

Like electric vehicles, hydrogen needs substantial infrastructure to work. Filling stations need the ability to store large volumes, typically in super cold liquid form and there needs to be enough locations that people can do the journeys they want to do.

Whereas with electric vehicles people can charge at home (even if it can be a little slow), hydrogen vehicles can't take off until there has been a huge investment in supporting infrastructure.

South Korea is leading the way globally with hydrogen infrastructure. Currently there are 45 hydrogen filling stations, growing to 310 by 2022[106]. This is still only a fraction of the 11,461 filling stations across the country[107]. Even in South Korea, a hydrogen leader, electrification seems to be taking an unrecoverable lead – by the end of 2021 there will be well over 12,000 super-fast electric car charging sites.

It is also notable that South Korea has seen several significant protests, following a fatal accident when a hydrogen filling station exploded. Public sentiment isn't wholly supportive of the push towards more hydrogen vehicles[108].

Hydrogen trains (rail travel is only responsible for 1% of transport emissions[109])

Hydrogen powered trains are already in operation in Germany and being trialled in the Netherlands and the UK[110]. The use of hydrogen in rail does have some potential in specific applications where electrification isn't cost effective. In the UK for example only 38% of the rail network is electrified[111] and in the US it is only 0.5%[112].

Trains can carry plenty of fuel and follow the same predictable routes. Fuel cell technology is of particular interest as 'electric' trains could take their electricity from a variety of sources – overhead lines, hydrogen fuel cells or batteries. This would continue an existing trend for trains capable of operating in different modes depending on where they are in the network[113].

Whilst electrification is probably the greenest option in most cases – the reality of installation costs for overhead lines along with genuine physical constraints (for example tunnel heights in existing tunnels) ill likely mean that in some cases hydrogen may be the best alternative.

Hydrogen ships (shipping is responsible for 10.6% of transport emissions[114])

Shipping is responsible for a significant contribution towards emissions. Ships often operate in international waters and as such it can be difficult for governments to legislate to lower emissions. Significant steps have recently been made to combat the impact on air quality from ships burning low quality, high sulphur 'bunker fuel'[115].

To further lower the carbon footprint from marine transport alternative fuels will be required. Hydrogen makes a lot of sense for marine applications and ammonia made from hydrogen has been often put forward as a potential future fuel option.

Ships have the benefit of having to call at a small number of ports; therefore, installation of the necessary infrastructure could start slowly. Ships capable of carrying larger loads and fuelling offshore may also help get the switch off the ground.

Already several ferry services are looking to trial hydrogen such as one in Scotland[116] and another in Norway[117].

Hydrogen trucks (trucks account for 29.4% of transport emissions[118])

Whilst electrification seems to be the likely pathway for passenger cars, trucks present a different challenge. Used to transport heavy loads, current battery technology just doesn't have enough stored energy to really work. Some expensive options have been suggested such as overhead lines[119] but there is not really a clear solution to decarbonising haulage other than hydrogen or synthetic fuels made from hydrogen.

There are several interesting research programmes in progress with haulage, such as the European Union's H2Haul project[120] which are trialling various hydrogen technologies to see whether hydrogen could work in the future.

Hydrogen for haulage has some real potential, as trucks tend to travel on main routes, filling up at specific sites for larger vehicles. Trucks may also follow regular predictable routes, from depot to depot, and as such targeted refuelling infrastructure could be used rather than the substantial investment to obtain a 'network effect' required by passenger vehicles.

Aviation (11.6% of transport emissions[121])

Aviation is one of the most challenging sectors to decarbonise. Existing safety performance is based on decades of fine-tuning supply chains and operations. Quite rightly few risks are taken with aircraft.

The aviation fuel used today has some excellent properties which make it perfect for flying, most notable it is very energy dense, and it is quite safe in and around aircraft as it doesn't catch fire too easily.

Hydrogen is exactly the opposite. It isn't very energy dense, and it catches fire in pretty much any mix with air. Aircraft powered by compressed or liquified hydrogen do seem to have more difficult safety and technical challenges to overcome compared to exiting technologies.

Example project: MR Hydra Ferry

The MF Hydra ferry in Norway[122] will run entirely on hydrogen, with an end-to-end supply chain set up to supply liquid hydrogen made through electrolysis at Linde's refinery in Germany.

A video showing the ferry in construction[123]:

18. Hydrogen in heating

Globally heating is responsible for 40% of all emissions and half of energy use[124]. The potential for our future heating needs to be met by hydrogen is increasingly widely discussed.

In the US half of homes are heated with natural gas, compared to 85% in the UK. These homes present significant challenges in achieving decarbonisation. Progress in natural gas technology has meant that the 'combi' boiler has become the dominant technology in the UK[125]. The recent ban on sales of gas boilers in the UK from 2025 is a huge step[126] – however what will replace them, remains unclear. Existing technologies are cheap and reliable, whereas future technology remains unproven and not necessarily cost effective for a broader role out.

When we consider heating and hot water, it is important to consider where we are today. Significant differences exist across the world in terms of system type, insulation, and ambient temperatures. What is right for one place is unlikely to be right for all.

Heating technology

The benefit of gas-based systems is that they can ramp up quickly when demand is high (opposed to heat pumps which can take hours or even days). Hydrogen is therefore a good replacement for an existing natural gas system. Several hydrogen boilers are being trialled. The first two properties in the world to run on pure hydrogen are planned to be built in Gateshead in the UK this year as part of a government funded trial[127] showing just how early this technology is in its development.

Managing the switchover

Technically a hydrogen switchover has some significant challenges. Most notably in how areas of the country are moved between the two incompatible gases. Existing natural gas boilers, cookers and fires will not be able to run on hydrogen. In fact, you couldn't switch over without knowing every property was isolated first.

The volume of work required to get an area ready for switchover would be massive. Technology will need to catch up to make a switchover manageable – such as boilers which could use either fuel enabling users just turn a switch on changeover day.

However even if you believe it is technically possible there remains some big challenges to a hydrogen switchover: Whilst engineers are focused on solving the technical problems it is also necessary to explore the social, economic, and environmental challenges, for example by answering the following questions:

- Who pays for a new boiler, cooker, gas fire (existing ones simply will not work) in every property? What if a resident wants a nicer looking cooker or fire than what is on offer?
- How will engineers who are currently qualified to work on natural gas systems (around 130,000 in the UK)[128] be retrained to work on both?
- How do we manage the switchover of large swathes of customers simultaneously whilst looking after the most vulnerable and limiting disruption?
- How do you deal with regional pricing (will hydrogen users pay more or even less per unit of heat than natural gas customers or heat pump users?)
- How will local air quality be managed? (hydrogen burns hotter so will produce

even more harmful nitrogen oxides than gas boilers do now).

Hydrogen and district heating

One solution to the challenges of switching over to local hydrogen networks is to use hydrogen for district heating. District heating is where hot water, typically 70 to 80 degrees Celsius (158F) is pumped around a network to distribute heat energy. This technology has been extensively used across the world with, for example ten million properties on such systems across Europe[129]. Currently most district heating systems are fed from combined heat and power engines (burning gas) or waste heat from industrial or waste processes. The carbon benefit of combined heat and power engines is decreasing as the electricity grid becomes greener and many of today's district heating systems will soon need to identify new sources of heat if they wish to reduce their carbon intensity.

District heating is an opportunity for hydrogen. If the source of the heat for the district can be replaced with either hydrogen boilers or fuel cells then a switch will comparatively far easier than replacing local networks, meters, and in-home appliances simultaneously.

Whilst the hydrogen system develops, district heating may be a useful interim step. This is of course if systems are installed 'hydrogen ready'. This would mean generation sites have adequate space to install hydrogen assets in the future along with spare flues for boilers and enough space to fit additional boilers in.

Making odourless hydrogen stinky!

In existing gas systems an odour is added to natural gas (methane). Mercaptan, which smells like rotten eggs is added so that if there is a leak, or simply a hob is left on by accident, our sensitive noses quickly smell the distinctive gas smell. Chemicals used to create an odour need some specific properties, most notable they need to be non-toxic, easily detectable by the human nose at low concentrations and to not damage equipment in the distribution system.

Hydrogen will need a unique 'smell' before it is pumped into houses. Studies in the UK have identified a number options, most notably odorant 'NB' which is already used in existing gas systems and would be recognisable to the public[130].

19. Electricity generation

Electricity generation is responsible for 37% of global emissions[131]. Emissions growth is primarily through additional coal generation being constantly installed which offsets renewable energy capacity installed elsewhere.

It's important to consider the source of hydrogen when using it for electricity generation – if you are not careful you could use hydrogen for electricity generation which is then used in electrolysis to make hydrogen – which would be quite an expensive way to make hydrogen!

Why would you use hydrogen for power generation?

This question has puzzled me quite a bit and when I recently asked it of my LinkedIn network the post quickly shot up to well over 15,000 views in a couple of hours and triggered a surprising amount of debate.

My question was particularly focused on why you would make blue hydrogen (hydrogen made from methane gas, with the carbon dioxide captured and stored underground) or green hydrogen (made from renewable electricity) to then combust it in a power station – when you could just burn methane in a traditional power station and capture the carbon dioxide after the event.

- **Pre vs post combustion capture**

Although post combustion carbon capture is possible it is not 100% perfect. To make carbon capture work the flue gas from the power station needs to be cleaned and then compressed (as it pretty much comes out at atmospheric pressure). The process also requires quite stable conditions – so the power station needs to be running in a steady state and not rapidly ramping up or down. From discussion it seems pre-combustion capture will likely be cleaner over all – as the process is simpler and doesn't involve the addition of other pollutants such as oxides of nitrogen (NOx) from the combustion process. It is however a very energy intensive way of going about it.

- Equipment

Capturing carbon dioxide from combustion requires lots of process equipment. This all-needs space and costs money. There are also hazards associated with it – potentially moving a plant from something which can operate largely autonomously to more of a chemical plant with associated risks. Capturing the carbon dioxide at the power station would also require a pipe route back to the storage site, whereas burning hydrogen would only require one pipe to get the hydrogen to the site.

- Hydrogen from far off places

In the future hydrogen may be generated at the source of the methane gas. So instead of transporting liquid gas such as LNG, the clean hydrogen is transported instead. This is also a good option for 'stranded gas' where there is no route to market and currently the gas is just flared (burned) or even worse vented. Currently 125 billion metres cubed of gas are vented or flared each year! Making hydrogen from this gas, rather than just burning it would be a far more environmentally friendly use if it were to be flared anyway.

Where a ready supply of global hydrogen is available, electricity generation from that hydrogen may very well make sense especially if the existing gas network has been re-purposed for hydrogen.

- **Flexibility**

Hydrogen generation via fuel cell or turbine will likely be far more flexible than a plant operating with carbon capture. Where an extensive hydrogen network existed, local hydrogen 'peaking' plants could be used to support the grid as demand changed. Due to the short operational runs, hydrogen would provide a green solution.

It's all about the comparative costs.

These decisions are largely about, fuel, investment, and operational costs. All of which remain largely unknown in the future and make it difficult to predict where the market will head. That said it's interesting to see where companies are heading. In the case of SSE and Equinor they are very much keeping their finger in both pies by looking to build both on one site. Although their timescales for the hydrogen generation plant are a little further out, aiming for 2030, than the CCGT (gas power station) with carbon capture, where they are aiming for 2025.

- Cost of electricity

Much of the discussion of hydrogen is around there being a 'glut' of green electricity at certain times of day making hydrogen almost free. Hydrogen power generation presents an opportunity to generate hydrogen when it is windy and sunny to then use for electricity generation at night or when it's not so windy. The economics of this are very much about the intraday costs of electricity, and in this case, it is very much battery technology which will be a direct competitor for hydrogen.

- Cost of hydrogen

As a global market for hydrogen develops the cost per kw will determine whether it's better to buy hydrogen or generate electricity a different way. There will need to be a fair playing field here as imported hydrogen will need to have a cost which recognises the carbon emitted in its manufacture (blue hydrogen is unlikely to be completely zero carbon).

- **Equipment costs**

The investments required are likely to be large. In deciding whether to use hydrogen or methane for electricity generation the comparative costs of the asset and the ongoing operations will become important. If the existing gas network has been re-purposed for hydrogen, then it may be easier to switch to hydrogen rather than install expensive new infrastructure for both gas and carbon dioxide. For reference a recent article from Argus highlighted that by 2025 combined cycle gas power stations with carbon capture could be cost effective. This came with a carbon price of around £35 per tonne.

Technology 'green swans'

In this area technology changes are rapid, and these can quickly tip the balance between one technology and another. With technology so young it's likely that across the whole sector there is plenty more disruption to come as costs are driven down in renewable generation, hydrogen production and energy use.

Will hydrogen really be used for generating electricity?

I still feel this is quite uncertain as to where the market will go. Currently hydrogen feels too costly to use as a gas substitute for power stations – and perhaps our effort should go to reducing the carbon impact of the hydrogen already used for fertiliser which already contributes to 2.5% of global emissions. I do feel this idea of a 'glut' of green renewable energy is a slight distraction, as more interconnected grids enable renewable electricity to reach more distant markets.

Plenty of projects are being announced so it will be interesting to see where they ultimately go!

Hydrogen would only make sense for large power stations in a situation where hydrogen was readily available – and uses where hydrogen could add the most benefit had been exhausted. It is more likely that rather than being used for 'baseload' generation, hydrogen could be used in a decentralised system through fuel cells and district heating. Once hydrogen distribution has been established it could replace existing combined, heat and power assets.

20. Making petrol from hydrogen

I have highlighted the challenges which batteries and hydrogen have with energy density and even suggested ammonia as a possible alternative. There is one tantalising prospect which I have not yet addressed, and this is of synthetic fuels.

The premise of synthetic fuels is that a liquid hydrocarbon can be formed from either biomass or reacting hydrogen with carbon dioxide. Currently alternative liquid fuels are generally biomass derivatives – it is however the fuels made from pure hydrogen, called e-fuels which provide an exciting prospect for decarbonising sectors which need a high-density source of energy.

The 2019 BP energy outlook puts global annual demand for transport fuels at just under 2000 million tonnes in 2035[132] a gradual climb from the 1500 million tonnes consumed now. The lions share being taken up with trucks and around a third by aviation and marine transport. Trucks, marine and aviation present the biggest challenge to decarbonisation – as currently there is no scalable green alternative primarily due to the energy density of the alternate sources of energy currently available. It is this energy density challenge that e-fuels present a potentially exciting solution.

How are e-fuels made?

To make e-fuels you need plenty of pure hydrogen and carbon monoxide. Carbon monoxide is made through passing Carbon dioxide through the excitingly called 'reverse water gas shift' reaction which uses electricity to split up the carbon dioxide molecules[133]. There are plenty of sources of carbon dioxide out there such as burning methane, coal or even biomass. The benefit of using that carbon dioxide in this process is it would not be released into the atmosphere straight away – and gets re-used.

The hydrogen, required in large volumes, would be more costly to find. However, in a hydrogen driven world the prospect of plentiful 'green' hydrogen produced from offshore wind, or solar in sunny places, through electrolysis is the most hopeful source. Alternatively, both the hydrogen and the carbon dioxide could be obtained from steam blasting methane. Wherever the hydrogen comes from the process is likely to be very energy intensive.

The final e-fuels process is called the Fischer-Tropsch[134] process. The process needs a catalyst such as cobalt, ruthenium or iron. The feedstock of pure hydrogen and carbon monoxide is reacted with the catalyst in a chamber under pressure – the output being pure liquid hydrocarbon. This process generates a lot of heat and it is this heat generation that makes the process quite inefficient as much of the energy available in the hydrogen molecules is lost as heat. If this heat can be used, for example in an industrial process or district heating then there is the opportunity to improve overall system efficiency.

Will e-fuels feature in the future?

Studies such as that by the Royal Society have put costs at around one and half euros a litre by 2050[135].

If legislation pushes trucks, aviation and marine to zero carbon then I believe that synthetic e-fuels will likely form part of the story. To what degree will depend on depth of decarbonisation and how competing technologies can push the energy density frontier. E-fuels success very much depends on whether road transport could be shifted to electrified rail or consumers move to shorter haul flights rather than long haul. There are simply too many scenarios or potential shifts to list here.

Finally, it is worth noting that the catalysts used in the process are hard to find and come with their own challenges. In particular cobalt mining has some important ethical considerations as does nickel of which the ruthenium is a by-product. It seems as with battery technology that all pathways need thinking about to be sustainable and not just low carbon.

Example project: Kalsruhe Germany

A pilot plant is being built in Karlsruhe, Germany. Costing 500 million Euros and capable of making 50,000 tonnes of synthetic fuel a year[136]. This seems quite a small volume compared to the five million tonnes of conventional fuels produced by that refinery annually. It is however interesting to see more industrial scale synthetic fuel plants being developed.

Shell has a video on making synthetic aviation fuel here[137]:

21. Some like it hot – is hydrogen the answer to those needing it a little warmer?

An often-overlooked group in our drive towards zero carbon heat, are industrial processes that need higher temperatures. Examples are steel making (over 1000°C), glass (melting temperature over 1400°C) and even plastics recycling. Heat pumps and heat networks only get you to sub hundred degree temperatures and certainly won't cut it for super high temperature industrial processes.

Substitution of products is an option – using less steel or more sustainable building materials for example. However, with increasing urbanisation the reality of the global economy is that there will remain a high demand for those materials used in building the cities of the future (steel, concrete, glass etc).

Globally steel making is responsible for 5% of emissions[138]. These are centred in locations where targeted carbon reduction interventions could make a genuine rapid dent in global emissions.

Can hydrogen get hot enough?

This is where there is real potential for hydrogen as a fuel. Hydrogen burns up to a cosy 2800°Celsius (about 700°Celsius simply burned in air) giving plenty of opportunities for supporting those needing something a little hotter.

We may be better off focusing our efforts on processes where hydrogen's potential can be realised – rather than on areas where other technologies are already proven (i.e., domestic heating where heat pumps and heat networks already show us an achievable pathway).

Couldn't we use the sun?

An interesting technology backed by Bill Gates[139] is a concentrated solar system from a company called Heliogen[140]. The system works by concentrating sunlight onto a single point to achieve temperatures more than 1500 degrees Celsius. The company suggests applications such as manufacturing concrete, steel, and petrochemicals and for treating waste. This technology has recently been named a best invention of 2020 by Time magazine certainly making it one to watch[141].

Example project: H2 Green Steel, Sweden

H2 Green Steel, a Swedish company has ambitious plans to build a brand-new steel plant, situated close to renewable energy sources in Sweden. Their aim is to be able to manufacture steel entirely from renewable energy – producing green hydrogen for their smelting processes. The plant is planned to be running by 2024[142].

A video about the plant can be found on their website[143]:

22. Could 'dirty' ammonia be the clean fuel of the future?

Globally the ammonia market is worth about thirty-three billion dollars accounting for a staggering 1.8% of global carbon emissions[144]. Produced under super high pressures from hydrogen and nitrogen; ammonia production is hugely energy intensive and more than a little bit 'dirty' when it comes to carbon emissions. Ammonia in liquid form provides a tantalising potential for a green fuel as it has a relatively high energy density of 3.4 kilowatts per litre, even if it does have a few challenges!

Could ammonia really be the fuel of the future? One of the biggest challenges of hydrogen as a fuel is its density in gaseous form along with high costs of storing and transporting it. Ammonia in liquid form provides a tantalising potential solution even if it does have a few challenges (being explosive, toxic, and very smelly). Potential early applications for ammonia as a fuel include shipping and maybe even aviation. I'm starting to think that maybe ammonia has the potential to be a 'black swan' technology in some specific sectors.

A 'black swan' event is something which is highly consequential but unlikely. These are often easily explainable – but only in retrospect.[145]

How is ammonia made?

The feed stock for ammonia is simply nitrogen and hydrogen. Nitrogen can be relatively efficiently extracted from the air through cryogenic processes (cooling the air so nitrogen drops out), whereas hydrogen is a bit trickier as I mentioned in previous chapters.

To create ammonia, those two gases are fed into a reactor and compressed to a high pressure in a process which has changed little in a hundred years called the Haber-Bosch process. In this process the hydrogen atoms from the feedstock are combined with nitrogen from the air. All of this is quite energy intensive as energy is needed to extract nitrogen as well as pump up the two gasses to such high pressures.

What about safety and the local environment?

Ammonia does come with its challenges. A quick web search on risks around ammonia gives you this:

'Exposure to high concentrations of ammonia in air causes immediate burning of the eyes, nose, throat and respiratory tract and can result in blindness, lung damage or death. Inhalation of lower concentrations can cause coughing, and nose and throat irritation'[146]

So not the nicest chemical to get exposed to! On top of the potential health impacts, it's also corrosive and explosive so presents some interesting challenges to engineers.

However, engineers are well used to handling such challenging chemicals, in fact in the United States there are already two thousand miles of ammonia pipelines along with a substantial infrastructure for ammonia manufacture and distribution. So, it's certainly not impossible that ammonia might be the right 'green' fuel for some applications.

In fact, existing hydrocarbons are distributed via pipelines, trucks, petrol stations etc. Petrol and diesel come with their own challenges in terms of environmental and explosion hazards.

Finally, ammonia is regularly used in refrigeration and heat pumps so it is highly likely you are passing near safely stored ammonia regularly in your everyday life at sites such as hospitals and supermarkets amongst many others.

This is of course all depends on the feedstock of hydrogen and nitrogen can be generated with no carbon emissions. Without a pathway to zero carbon hydrogen and nitrogen there is no zero-carbon ammonia.

Would ammonia be more expensive than hydrogen?

A study by the Royal Society[147] highlighted substantial savings using ammonia in rail, shipping and heavy road transport. In fact, nearly eighty percent less than that of hydrogen gas and a third of the costs of liquefied hydrogen.

It is perhaps these three areas where ammonia has some interesting potential as a fuel for the future. Shipping is likely to be the first – with some projections from the likes of the American Bureau of Shipping suggesting that by 2050 over 30% of marine traffic will be ammonia fuelled[148].

Ammonia's potential is on the side of a hydrogen economy filling in the gaps for hydrogen. For some applications hydrogen just is not going to work and this is where Ammonia may be able to step in and offer an alternative.

How green could ammonia be?

Ammonia could absolutely be zero carbon. If you can make green hydrogen (either with green electricity or carbon capture and storage) and green electricity you can make green ammonia. You just need a lot of green energy. I do think the focus now should be on de-carbonising the world's existing ammonia demand. This would then provide a sound footing for ammonia to potentially be used as a green fuel.

Example project: The Ship 'Viking Energy'

A marine support vessel 'Viking Energy' is being converted to run on Ammonia fuel cells.
Chemical giant Yara will provide the green ammonia for the ship operated by Equinor (formerly Statoil)[149]. The ship is expected to be at sea and operating fully on Ammonia by 2024.

Part 5: The future energy system

23. Hydrogen provenance

In a global interconnected system understanding where hydrogen has come from will become incredibly important. The temptation for some to make hydrogen from coal and release the carbon dioxide into the atmosphere may be too great. Whilst hydrogen projects remain small and directly linked this won't be too much of a problem, however as international trade[150] develops the risk increases.

Already some have proposed using blockchain to verify hydrogen provenance and systems are already in production[151]. How such a system is administered is incredibly important – too onerous and the cost burden of tracking will reduce the speed to technology uptake, too loose and public faith in hydrogen will be quickly shaken. The trust of the global public is incredibly important as has been demonstrated in the role out of other sustainability programmes – waste recycling in the UK is a fine example of where reality has the potential to undermine trust[152] as plastics diligently sorted by the public have ended up in landfill along with unsorted waste.

It is inevitable that a certification scheme will need to be developed otherwise it won't be long before hydrogen generates as much scandal as the carbon it saves.

The following would be key elements of a hydrogen carbon labelling system:

Validation of the source

End consumers will need to be sure about source. Although this feels simple in practice it could become incredibly complicated. In the Middle East hydrogen produced from solar could quickly be mixed with hydrogen produced from methane (hopefully with carbon capture). This cargo is then passed from owner to owner until it reaches it point of delivery. The cargo may have an average carbon intensity, but the person buying 100% green hydrogen will want to know that it is green hydrogen that they are getting. Source validation becomes incredibly important particularly given the economic benefits of just using methane and blasting the carbon dioxide straight into the atmosphere.

Transportation and storage

Understanding carbon intensity won't just stop at manufacture. How hydrogen is transported to its destination may have a significant impact on its intensity. Where energy is used to compress or liquify the hydrogen then the carbon intensity of that energy needs to be considered. If hydrogen is lost to atmosphere during transport, then the global warming effect of that hydrogen must be included in the carbon intensity calculation.

This makes carbon assessment incredibly complicated as it is not just a certificate of manufacture required but also a certificate of shipping.

Recognition of carbon intensity in the pricing

The system can't just rely on goodwill. Somehow the carbon intensity of the hydrogen needs reflecting in the price. Whilst some are happy to pay more, this has a threshold where the additional cost is just too much. If the delta in cost between green and dirty hydrogen isn't enough then there is a risk dirty hydrogen just replaces dirty gas.

Openness and communication

There needs to be a recognition that hydrogen isn't perfectly green. Hydrogen lost along its journey adds to global warming and carbon, capture and storage isn't perfect. Consumers need to be treated like intelligent buyers and given the information they need to understand.

A useful analogy is in the communication around eggs. Consumers are now much savvier in understanding the conditions of the birds producing the eggs we eat. There may be 11 billion eggs eaten in the United Kingdom each year, but with a strong communication system it is possible for consumers to understand what they are buying[153]. This has been achieved through strong simple messaging.

Where this gets harder in both eggs and hydrogen is third parties. Whilst relatively easy to achieve in our homes it is less easy to verify in businesses that we visit. When they have a fried egg sandwich in a café, do consumers apply the same standards they would to a box of eggs they would buy from a shop themselves. Similarly, when you go to a supermarket, or fly on an airplane it is simply not realistic to expect consumers to be able to understand and influence the energy supply to all the businesses they use. Whilst some steps can be made to inform consumer choice, regulation will likely be needed in some sectors.

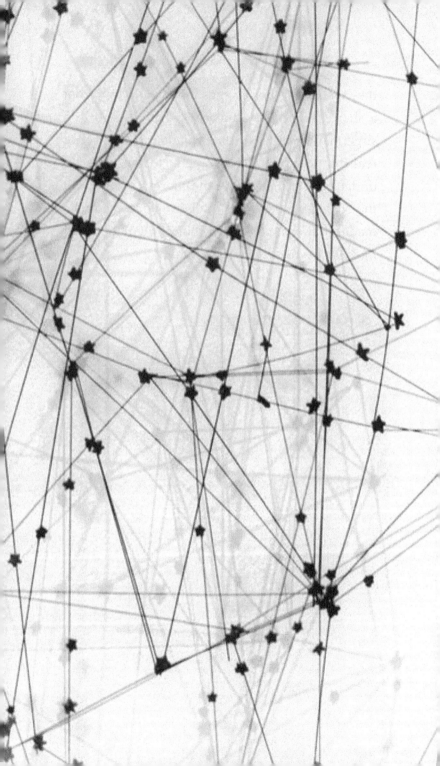

24. An integrated energy system

As with everything in energy, hydrogen cannot exist in isolation. It is itself purely a carrier for energy and a future hydrogen system is likely to be hugely complex. Hydrogen production, storage and distribution assets are also unlikely to come cheap and as such a transition to a hydrogen energy system will need huge investment. In the UK switching over the gas system to hydrogen for heating alone has a price tag of £50 billion to £100 billion and that assumes a supply of hydrogen is available to feed into the system[154]. Any future hydrogen system is not going to come cheap, and it is going to have to form part of an integrated generation, distribution, and storage system.

Hydrogen will have complex economic drivers, many of which are not currently well understood. Costs of production and transport will impact where hydrogen is produces, along with access to either natural gas (hopefully with a local carbon store) or green electricity.

Distribution costs will vary depending on whether the hydrogen gas can be transported via pipeline or needs cryogenically cooling to be transported as a liquid. Whereas in hydrocarbons decades of innovation and development have provided a stable environment for investment hydrogen is very much in its formative years and investment will be full of both opportunity and risk.

Balancing demand from heating and transport

The current energy system largely detaches heating demand from transport. Liquid hydrocarbons are used for transport and methane gas for heating. Sudden peaks in demand for one don't immediately impact the other. The electricity system again has very little impacting it from transport. This is of course changing rapidly with increasing demand from electric vehicles on the system.

The two systems being largely detached all changes with a fully integrated hydrogen system. It is likely that electricity demand will peak in similar months to hydrogen and as such during times of high electricity demand (therefore expensive) it won't be economic to produce local hydrogen. Hydrogen storage is therefore essential to ensuring that the system can cope.

Similarly, hydrogen demand from transport will be competing with hydrogen for heating. As hydrogen gets pulled towards essential heating would we be happy to see supplies for the transport sector impacted?

Access to carbon free electricity

Any hydrogen system which relies on local production will need to be near a source of low or carbon free electricity. This electricity needs to be available in an appropriate volume and price to make it worth using for hydrogen locally. It may be that hydrogen enables a route to market for places far away from consumers. For example, offshore wind in northern Scotland or solar in the Sahara. Whilst long distance transmission cables for electricity may be costly or not technically feasible – a liquified hydrogen route may be possible. This is in a similar way in which liquid natural gas currently enables gas to be produced in Eastern Russia[155], Northern Australia[156] and the far North of Norway[157].

Accessing carbon storage.

Where the hydrogen is made from natural gas a route to suitable carbon capture sites is essential. There is also a potential synergy here with high energy users such as steel or glass manufacture. Where a carbon dioxide transmission system is in place you could see the potential for pockets of energy intensive industries to be established, like Hynet in the UK[158] where the proposal is to integrate hydrogen generation and distribution alongside carbon capture and storage into an integrated system.

Is there a natural symbiosis with electrification?

Rather than being competitors could hydrogen infrastructure complement electric vehicle infrastructure? Whilst light vehicles may be more likely to be battery powered in the future, heavy trucks are a little more difficult to decarbonise and therefore it is likely that an alternative will be needed to batteries for those harder to decarbonise parts of the fleet. This may be hydrogen.

PEM (polymer electrolyte membrane) electrolysis technology uses container based modular units, with relatively maintenance free technology. What they do need is a ready supply of electricity and lots of it. In a hydrogen world filling stations may be able to generate their hydrogen locally (rather than needing to be supplied by tanker) using PEM electrolysis – however this will very certainly need large connections to the electricity grid.

Fast EV charging stations in the future will also need to have big grid connections. With more and more electric vehicles on the road these connections are going to get bigger and bigger – especially with some chargers packing an impressive 350-kilowatt compared to a tiny 7-kilowatt home charger, for just one charge point. The grid connection won't be consistently used as cars come and go and the larger fast ones are very unlikely to be used overnight. The potential exists to use that grid capacity to generate hydrogen. This hydrogen could then be stored ready for when a vehicle arrived which needed it. Filling stations of the future could therefore deliver both electric vehicle and hydrogen charging – the hydrogen being generated overnight when the grid capacity isn't being used.

Finally, if there was more electricity demand than the grid could deliver, or electricity was extremely expensive, the hydrogen could be put back through a fuel cell to charge the vehicle. Thus, for transport, hydrogen and electrification might not be competitors but symbiotic partners – relying on each other to deliver their form of energy. Charging electric vehicles and filling hydrogen trucks may well be done in the same place sharing the same gird connection, but with the technologies symbiotically linked to deliver the optimum outcome.

Perhaps the future energy system isn't about hydrogen vs electrification but rather how technologies work hand in hand?

The future of energy: hydrogen

25. Is hydrogen the chicken or the egg?

In this book I have repeated several times that over 95% of hydrogen produced today is exceptionally carbon intensive. In managing the transition this presents society with a unique challenge. Should we decarbonise the hydrogen we produce today first, before growing hydrogen demand, or do we grow demand whilst reducing hydrogen carbon intensity over time.

In scenario one, global political intervention would be required to drive down emissions, effectively banning steam methane reformation of gas and coal without carbon capture. This would drive up the global cost of hydrogen considerably in the short term.

In scenario two, we wait. Global carbon intensity of hydrogen is unlikely to fall quickly. Much of the supply for new demand would likely be met through carbon intensive processes for the next five to ten years - risking emitting far more carbon than had we have sought an interim step to cleaner fuels.

There is a third way – one in which hydrogen labelling becomes a key element of hydrogen use. Guaranteeing end to end provenance of hydrogen becomes hugely important to avoid 'green technologies' hiding behind the green hydrogen story when in fact the truth is far murkier.

Technologies such as blockchain could be used to enable end to end certification of hydrogen. Hydrogen producers sell into a market their hydrogen based on carbon intensity, enabling users and regulators to be crystal clear on the carbon intensity of the hydrogen being used.

When progressing down the hydrogen path, reducing cost and emissions rapidly is incredibly important – therefore it is essential that new additional to hydrogen demand push low carbon hydrogen generation on, whilst discouraging existing dirty methods.

Without adequate controls there is a risk of being caught in a 'bait and switch'[159] in which hydrogen demand is rapidly increased early – but cost and carbon are not reduced. Strong international cooperation and regulation is therefore required to prevent this taking place.

Part 6: What's next for hydrogen?

26. Scaling up

With the right regulatory and economic environment hydrogen technology is on the brink of rapidly scaling up. The large number of projects highlighted in the proceeding chapters demonstrate how quickly hydrogen is scaling up – and it's clear that it is not from a standing start – however that maturity very much depends on where in the hydrogen supply chain you look.

Production

The technology clearly is already well established for making hydrogen from methane, and there are already plenty of electrolysis examples – albeit generating significantly less than the more well-established steam methane reformation process.

Additionally, there are plenty of clean electricity project out there that show that green electricity can be produced to make green hydrogen. There are also plenty of examples where carbon dioxide has been captured and stored in long term underground storage.

The technology for the production part of the supply chain is there and read for scaling.

Transport & distribution

Like in hydrogen production, there are already plenty of industrial scale examples of hydrogen being stored and transported. Already hydrogen is distributed extensively across pipe systems over thousands of kilometres. Hydrogen is already stored as a liquid in huge volumes deep underground and is stored on the surface both as a liquid and a pressurised gas.

Consumption

It is the consumption part of the supply chain where hydrogen is less well developed. Whilst hydrogen cars, boats and trains all exist, their numbers are limited. Similarly, it is only recently that boilers for homes have become available.

In summary scaling of hydrogen may come not from the supply side but that of the demand. There is currently plenty of hydrogen around (even if some of it isn't very green) to enable a hydrogen economy to develop, there just isn't the demand case.

The future of energy: hydrogen

27. Competition with hydrogen

Hydrogen doesn't exist in isolation. In each use case there are many competitors and incumbent technologies. Technologies succeed due to either consumer behaviour or regulation. Whilst hydrogen for home heating requires significant direct regulatory intervention to force a switch, hydrogen vehicles are more about consumer choice between competing technologies.

Transport – Light vehicles

Overall, globally electric vehicles seem well ahead of those powered by hydrogen – with hydrogen unlikely to gain much market share. The relative efficiency of hydrogen vs electric vehicles makes it difficult to see a justifiable case for road transport. Whilst the overall efficiency of electric vehicles from the wind turbine to kilometres on the road is around seventy to eighty percent, hydrogen is down around twenty to thirty[160]. There has also been substantial investment in electric vehicles by manufacturers such as Nissan, Tesla, and BMW with over 15 mass produced models on the market[161]. Meanwhile hydrogen vehicles haven't seen anywhere near the same amount of investment or uptake.

Whilst electric vehicle infrastructure may lag demand a little, anyone who buys an electric vehicle can charge from home which suits them for most journeys, however with hydrogen there needs to be a certain base level of infrastructure before anyone other than niche users would invest. It seems therefore that the cards are stacked against hydrogen in the light vehicle market for now.

Transport – Haulage, rail and marine

Hydrogen has more potential in heavy haulage, marine and rail. Current battery energy density makes the electrification of trucks difficult and expensive. Some countries have proposed overhead wires (like trams); however, these systems are complex to install and would likely to be limited to specific use cases.

Domestic and commercial heating

Hydrogen's direct competitor in heating is heat pumps. Heat pumps use electricity efficiently by adding units of energy from either the ground or the outside air. Currently both ground and air source heat pumps are bulky and expensive and often require changes to the existing heating systems. Hydrogen presents an alternative to these for heating without these challenges at point of use. Appliances may need to be changed but would be largely similar in size and performance. For heating the challenge of getting hydrogen to the point-of-use is the bigger hurdle to overcome along with the cost effectiveness compared to already well-developed heat pump technology.

Heavy industry

Steel making and processes requiring high temperatures are two of the most likely applications for large scale hydrogen use. There are no credible alternatives to decarbonising these applications and hydrogen is highly likely to be the leader in securing lower carbon pathways for these.

Fertiliser (ammonia)

Finally, fertiliser is already a huge hydrogen user. To achieve any kind of credible lower carbon world either less ammonia-based fertiliser will need to be used or the hydrogen consumed in manufacturing the ammonia will need to be made a lot greener. With population growth using less fertiliser is unlikely and therefore an increase in the use of green hydrogen technologies is extremely likely in this area.

28. Conclusion

When I sat to write this book, I came to the topic a hydrogen sceptic. As engineers often do – I could see more problems than solutions. As I have researched the various elements my scepticism softened as I began to realise that hydrogen is not a source of energy, but a way to move it around. In a system where storage and intensity matter hydrogen has some properties which its competitors can't always beat. Therefore, I think as a technology it will play a part in our future lives. I don't think it is the 'silver bullet' which solves all our problems; however, I do think that in certain applications it presents a pathway to lower carbon which other technologies simply can't achieve. I do believe that the existing carbon footprint from today's hydrogen production needs addressing, or hydrogen's green image risks being tarnished before the technology has got off the ground.

I opened the book with some discussion of consumer engagement and understanding. I believe this remains a huge challenge at all levels of the hydrogen system. There is simply not enough understanding across all areas of society of hydrogen as a technology for moving and transporting energy. This will need to change in the coming years if the technology is to have any chance of success.

Furthermore, investors will need certainty from government to plough huge amounts of money into infrastructure. It is that regulatory certainty which in turns drives inevitability. Similarly, to guarantees already given to nuclear power stations[162] or offshore wind[163], hydrogen will likely need some sort of commitment from governments of ongoing demand and prices. Multi-billion-pound investments such as those required for hydrogen manufacture and distribution can't be done speculatively. This is where there comes a 'chicken and egg' scenario where hydrogen needs to be made a reality in regulation, before it's proven in practice.

Hydrogen remains a deeply complex topic in energy. Multiple permutations of generation, distribution and use mean that it's almost impossible to predict how an integrated hydrogen system will establish. Much of what we read on the topic is over simplified, with flippant reporting which means that the public remains lost in understanding this emerging range of technologies.

To move from the periphery of the energy landscape to the core much needs to be done to educate and inform. As has been seen globally a rush towards hydrogen comes with its challenges and risks – whilst some sectors such as generation or industry don't necessarily rely on public engagement, transport and heating do.

Whilst in its infancy hydrogen is very much here to stay. However competing technologies and unpredictable costs make it challenging for investors to engage in the market, whilst consumers remain largely passive.

I would like to see decarbonisation of existing hydrogen consumption, before moving to more exotic applications. The staggering amount of dirty hydrogen used today can't be sustained and if this was to be made through lower carbon methods could quickly make a huge difference to global emissions now. This would also stimulate investment in green (and blue) hydrogen technologies.

To finish I'd like to make some bold predictions. In a few years no doubt I will reflect on these with amusement! In 2031 I believe the following will be happening:

- Battery technology will remain dominant for cars, vans, and buses.
- Some areas will have hydrogen for home heating. Particularly the northern areas of the UK and Europe where existing hydrogen projects will become established.
- Air travel will move to be more regional based and hybrid aircraft capable of shorter flights. Using a combination of batteries and hydrogen will become common place.
- Large scale hydrogen production will take place using a mixture of blue and green hydrogen technologies in the Middle East and parts of Africa.
- A global trade in green hydrogen will be established with hydrogen being moved between manufacturing and demand centres.

I have hugely enjoyed researching and pulling this book together. I hope I have given an interesting and enlightening tour of a complex topic, and not made it too dry. I intend to update this book as the technology and use of hydrogen develops. More projects will come on-line and 'green swans' will definitely emerge as investment continues. I certainly look forward to seeing where hydrogen technology will emerge in our energy system in the coming years.

Please do contact me with any thoughts, comments, or corrections on this book or the energy system in general. All feedback goes into improving the future of energy books and is greatly appreciated.

29. Hydrogen projects

The International Energy Agency (IEA) maintain a database of hydrogen projects[164]. As of March 2021, there are 448 projects in the database. A useful summary of the top 22 gigawatt plus hydrogen projects is provided on the website 'recharge'[165].

Here are some of the highlights:

NortH2

The joint objective is to set up large-scale green hydrogen production using offshore wind power. As much as 4 gigawatts by 2030, in fact, which will fulfil one of the goals set by the Dutch climate agreement. But the ambition goes further than that. NortH2 wants to upscale to more than 10 gigawatts by 2040. By then, green hydrogen output, which will initially be produced in Eemshaven and later possibly offshore as well, will total around one million metric tons on an annual basis, cutting carbon emissions by over eight to ten megatons a year. Backed by the Groningen provincial authority, NortH2 does not rule out other serious partners joining the project further down the line.

www.north2.eu

The Asian Renewable Energy Hub

The Asian Renewable Energy Hub will generate 26 gigawatts of renewable energy in Western Australia. Up to three gigawatts of generation capacity will be dedicated to large energy users in the Pilbara region, which could include new and expanded mines and downstream mineral processing. The bulk of the energy will be used for large scale production of green hydrogen products for domestic and export markets.

asianrehub.com

HyNet - North West Region, United Kingdom

Based on the production of hydrogen from natural gas. It includes the development of a new hydrogen pipeline; and the creation of the UK's first carbon capture, and storage (CCS) infrastructure. CCS is a vital technology to achieve the widespread emissions savings needed to meet the 2050 carbon reduction targets.

hynet.co.uk

BP – Teeside, United Kingdom

Proposed project in Teesside would be the largest in the UK, producing up to one gigawatt of 'blue' hydrogen – 20% of the UK's hydrogen target – by 2030 and supporting development of region as UK's first hydrogen transport hub.

30. Energy units

Energy is typically measured in watts. Unfortunately, one watt is an incredibly small measure and so to make energy numbers useable engineers use multiples of a thousand watts to talk about energy (Kilo, Mega, Giga and Tera).

To make matters even more confusing we then distinguish between 'instantaneous' energy use and total energy used. Where total is required hours are added to the units for example on energy bills.

Hopefully the list below helps make this clearer.

Watts

A typical energy saving light bulb uses around 6 watts (6w). Running the light bulb for a day uses 144Wh (which is more commonly described as 0.14 kWh).

Kilowatts (kw): 1,000 Watts (Most commonly used for domestic energy)

A domestic oven uses 3kW. Running the oven for two hours uses 6kwh.

Megawatts (MW): 1,000 Kilowatts (Most commonly used for power generation and distribution)

Gigawatts (GW): 1,000 Megawatts (used to describe national demand)

The typical instantaneous demand for electricity in the UK is around 40 gigawatts (GW).

Terawatts (TW): 1000 Gigawatts (A big number. Used to describe country level consumption)

Annual UK electricity consumption is 310 Terawatt Hours (TWh)

Energy in hydrogen: 1Kg of hydrogen contains 33.33kwh of energy[166].

Hydrogen gas: 1Kg occupies 11m3

Compressed hydrogen: At 700Bar (700 times atmospheric pressure) 42Kg of hydrogen occupies 1m3.

Liquified hydrogen[167]: 71Kg of hydrogen occupies a m3.

31. Measuring greenhouse gases

Carbon intensity

- 1 cup of coffee – 21g[168]
- A cheeseburger – 4kg[169] (of which 2.6kg is from cattle flatulence and waste!)
- 1 hour of surgery under anaesthetic 24Kg[170]
- Return flight London to New York – 1.6 Tonnes (8 Tonnes if first class)[171]
- Train trip London to Paris – 4.1kg [172]
- Average UK citizen – 5.3 tonnes[173]
- UK annual emissions – 435 million tonnes carbon dioxide equivalent [174]
- Global greenhouse gas emissions annually: 36 billion tonnes[175]

Volumetric measures of carbon dioxide

- 1.964 kg or CO2 fills a square meter at room temperature.
- 56kg of CO2 to fill a double decker bus.[176]

Global warming potential

In discussing global warming, most conversation are focused on carbon dioxide. However, lots of gases cause a far worse effect if released direct to atmosphere. This effect is measured as 'global warming potential' and typically looks at the effect over 100 years.

- Ammonia: 0.0 [177]
- Carbon dioxide: 1.0
- Hydrogen: 5.8[178]
- Methane (natural gas): 38-46[179]
- Nitrous oxide: 265-298[180]

32. Hydrogen colour chart

ZERO/VERY LOW CARBON

Green hydrogen: Made through electrolysis using renewable electricity. Electricity is used to split water into hydrogen and oxygen.

Blue hydrogen: Grey, brown, or black hydrogen but with the carbon dioxide stored deep underground through 'carbon capture and storage' (CCS).

Pink hydrogen: Produced like green hydrogen through electrolysis but solely using energy from nuclear power.

Yellow hydrogen: Produced like green hydrogen through electrolysis but solely using energy from solar power.

White hydrogen: Hydrogen made from carbohydrate (so potatoes or crops!).

MEDIUM TO HIGH CARBON EMISSIONS

Turquoise hydrogen: Produced through pyrolysis. In pyrolysis instead of polluting CO_2 gas a solid carbon by-product is produced. The feedstock is methane of even waste plastics. Pyrolysis works by heating products to an extremely high temperature in an inert atmosphere. The emissions relate to the fuel needed to provide heat for the process.

Gold hydrogen: Hydrogen produced from naturally occurring deposits in sedimentary rock.

HIGH CARBON EMISSIONS

Grey hydrogen: Hydrogen made from natural gas in a process called steam reformation with no CCS.

VERY HIGH CARBON EMISSIONS

Black hydrogen: Made from Coal (in a process like grey hydrogen) with no CCS. Even more carbon intensive than grey hydrogen.

Brown hydrogen: Made from lignite (in a process like grey hydrogen) with no CCS. Even more carbon intensive than black and grey hydrogen. Lignite is compressed peat and generates a lot of carbon dioxide when combusted.

33. Useful resources

The following provide some excellent and regularly updated information:

Bloomberg New Energy Finance: about.bnef.com

Energy Central: www.energycentral.com

Hydrogen Council: www.hydrogencouncil.com

International Energy Agency: www.iea.org their hydrogen projects database
https://www.iea.org/reports/hydrogen-projects-database

National Grid Future Energy Scenarios: fes.nationalgrid.com

Shell Energy Scenarios: www.shell.com/energy-and-innovation/the-energy-future/scenarios.html

Sustainable Energy Without the Hot Air: www.withoutthehotair.co.uk

World Economic Forum: www.weforum.org

34. Photo credits

All images are courtesy of the wonderful unsplash (www.unsplash.com), iStock or are the author's own.

35. About the author

John Armstrong is an engineer whose career has spanned the extremes of the energy industry – giving him a front seat on the energy rollercoaster. He began his career in oil and gas, before moving to work across fossil and renewable electricity generation. More recently John has been leading the growth of decentralised energy and district heating in the UK and now manages energy infrastructure assets.

John lives in Wiltshire near Bath with his wife and two daughters.

36. References

[1] https://www.theagilityeffect.com/en/review/is-hydrogen-a-miracle-solution-in-the-fight-against-climate-change/

[2] https://www.ncl.ac.uk/media/wwwnclacuk/geographypoliticsandsociology/files/news/blended-hydrogen-the-uk-publics-perspective.pdf

[3] https://www.airbus.com/newsroom/stories/hydrogen-aviation-understanding-challenges-to-widespread-adoption.html

[4] https://www.reuters.com/article/us-autos-hydrogen-southkorea-insight-idUSKBN1W936A

[5] https://hbr.org/sponsored/2021/03/how-japans-hydrogen-innovations-may-fuel-cleaner-days-ahead

[6] https://www.iea.org/reports/hydrogen-projects-database

[7] https://pubchem.ncbi.nlm.nih.gov/element/Hydrogen#section=Ionization-Energy

[8] https://www.airships.net/hindenburg/disaster/

[9] https://ourworldindata.org/how-many-people-does-synthetic-fertilizer-feed

[10] https://www.geos.ed.ac.uk/~dstevens/Presentations/Papers/derwent_ijhr06.pdf

[11] https://www.epa.gov/ghgemissions/understanding-global-warming-potentials#:~:text=Methane%20(CH4)%20is%20estimated,uses%20a%20different%20value.).

[12] https://www.iea.org/fuels-and-technologies/hydrogen#key-findings

[13] https://www.iea.org/reports/the-future-of-hydrogen

[14]https://www.prnewswire.com/news-releases/global-ammonia-market-is-projected-to-grow-and-cross--68-billion-by-2025-301105553.html

[15] https://ammoniaindustry.com/

[16]https://www.grandviewresearch.com/press-release/global-ammonia-market#:~:text=The%20global%20ammonia%20market%20was,5.3%25%20from%202017%20to%202025.&text=Asia%20Pacific%20dominated%20the%20industry,region%20over%20the%20forecast%20period

[17]https://www.eia.gov/todayinenergy/detail.php?id=24612#:~:text=Refineries%20use%20hydrogen%20to%20lower%20the%20sulfur%20content%20of%20diesel%20fuel.&text=Refineries%20also%20produce%20some%20by,fraction%20of%20their%20hydrogen%20needs.

[18]https://www.mckinsey.com/industries/oil-and-gas/our-insights/petroleum-blog/diesel-demand-still-growing-globally-despite-dieselgate

[19]https://www.iea.org/data-and-statistics/charts/global-electrolysis-capacity-becoming-operational-annually-2014-2023-historical-and-announced

[20]https://www.energy.gov/eere/fuelcells/hydrogen-pipelines

[21]https://www.ncl.ac.uk/media/wwwnclacuk/geographypoliticsandsociology/files/news/blended-hydrogen-the-uk-publics-perspective.pdf

[22] https://www.weforum.org/agenda/2019/04/why-dont-the-public-see-hydrogen-as-a-safe-energy-source/#:~:text=One%20major%20reason%20is%20the%20public%20perception%20of%20hydrogen%20safety.&text=Among%20those%20who%20believed%20hyd

rogen,thought%20it%20was%20very%20dangerous.

[23]https://www.ncl.ac.uk/media/wwwnclacuk/geograph ypoliticsandsociology/files/news/blended-hydrogen-the-uk-publics-perspective.pdf

[24]https://www.forbes.com/sites/mikescott/2020/12/14/g reen-hydrogen-the-fuel-of-the-future-set-for-50-fold-expansion/?sh=76524d286df3

[25]https://www.ncl.ac.uk/media/wwwnclacuk/geograph ypoliticsandsociology/files/news/blended-hydrogen-the-uk-publics-perspective.pdf

[26] https://heattrust.org/

[27] https://www.livescience.com/28466-hydrogen.html

[28]https://www.enapter.com/hydrogen-clearing-up-the-colours

[29]https://www.carbonbrief.org/solar-wind-nuclear-amazingly-low-carbon-footprints

[30]https://www.forbes.com/sites/rrapier/2020/06/06/esti mating-the-carbon-footprint-of-hydrogen-production/?sh=9fb892024bd6

[31]http://valvemagazine.com/web-only/categories/technical-topics/10419-hydrogen-s-role-in-reducing-industrial-carbon-emissions.html

[32] https://www.iea.org/reports/the-future-of-hydrogen

[33] https://www.iea.org/reports/the-future-of-hydrogen

[34] https://www.irena.org/publications/2020/Dec/Green-hydrogen-cost-reduction

[35]https://www.solarpowerportal.co.uk/news/solar_pv_ costs_fall_82_over_the_last_decade_says_irena#:~:text= A%20new%20report%20by%20the,PV%20globally%20 dropped%20by%2082%25.&text=In%202019%20alone %2C%20the%20cost,five%20pence%20per%20kilowatt

%2Dhour.

[36]https://www.carbontrust.com/resources/policy-innovation-and-cost-reduction-in-uk-offshore-wind

[37]https://www.sciencedirect.com/topics/engineering/methane-steam-reforming

[38]www.fossiltransition.org/pages/post_combustion_capture_/128.php

[39]www.drax.com/technology/how-do-you-store-co2-and-what-happens-to-it-when-you-do/

[40]www.carbonbrief.org/world-can-safely-store-billions-tonnes-co2-underground

[41] www.gov.uk/government/news/pm-outlines-his-ten-point-plan-for-a-green-industrial-revolution-for-250000-jobs

[42]https://www.equinor.com/en/what-we-do/h2hsaltend.html

[43]https://www.energy.gov/eere/fuelcells/hydrogen-production-electrolysis

[44]http://valvemagazine.com/web-only/categories/technical-topics/10419-hydrogen-s-role-in-reducing-industrial-carbon-emissions.html

[45] https://cleanenergypartnership.de/en/faq/hydrogen-production-and-storage/#:~:text=To%20produce%201%20kg%20of%20hydrogen%2C%20nine%20times%20the%20amount,is%20necessary%2C%20i.e.%20nine%20litres.

[46]https://www.city.ac.uk/news/2019/october/one-hamburger-takes-2,400-litres-hidden-water-make#:~:text='Water%20has%20been%20fed%20into,'

[47]http://hybalance.eu/hybalance/short-presentation/about-pem-electrolysis/

[48]https://www.sciencedirect.com/topics/engineering/alkaline-water-electrolysis

[49]https://nj.gov/health/eoh/rtkweb/documents/fs/1571.pdf

[50]https://iopscience.iop.org/article/10.1088/1755-1315/371/4/042022/pdf

[51]https://iopscience.iop.org/article/10.1088/1755-1315/371/4/042022/pdf

[52] https://www.bbc.co.uk/news/business-55763356

[53]https://refhyne.eu/shell-starts-up-europes-largest-pem-green-hydrogen-electrolyser/

[54] https://refhyne.eu/news-item-heading/

[55]https://www.azocleantech.com/article.aspx?ArticleID=336

[56]https://www.basf.com/gb/en/who-we-are/sustainability/we-produce-safely-and-efficiently/energy-and-climate-protection/carbon-management/interview-methane-pyrolysis.html

[57]https://www.energylivenews.com/2020/08/25/uks-first-plastic-to-hydrogen-project-moves-forward-in-cheshire/

[58]https://pubs.acs.org/doi/10.1021/acs.energyfuels.0c02043

[59]https://www.luxresearchinc.com/blog/technology-landscape-key-players-in-methane-pyrolysis

[60]   https://www.greencarcongress.com/2010/06/elbaba-20100611.html

[61] https://youtu.be/4bAmtwwMmpY

[62]https://www.energy.gov/eere/fuelcells/hydrogen-pipelines

[63]https://pulsenews.co.kr/view.php?year=2019&no=346

776

[64]https://www.energynetworks.org/newsroom/hydrog
en-blending-what-is-it-and-why-does-it-matter
[65]https://www1.eere.energy.gov/hydrogenandfuelcells/
tech_validation/pdfs/fcm01r0.pdf
[66]https://www.independent.co.uk/news/uk/home-
news/what-exactly-mercaptan-8462250.html
[67]https://h2tools.org/bibliography/fuel-cells-and-
odorants-hydrogen
[68]https://www.geos.ed.ac.uk/~dstevens/Presentations/P
apers/derwent_ijhr06.pdf
[69] https://www.epa.gov/ghgemissions/understanding-
global-warming-
potentials#:~:text=Methane%20(CH4)%20is%20estimat
ed,uses%20a%20different%20value.).
[70]https://www.ch-iv.com/all-about-
lng/#:~:text=Your%20LNG%20Experts,at%20a%20stove
%20burner%20tip.
[71]https://www.marinetraffic.com/en/ais/details/ships/s
hipid:712524/mmsi:538003212/imo:9337755/vessel:MO
ZAH
[72] https://www.youtube.com/watch?v=WGPkSuIH7uA
[73]https://www.siemens-
energy.com/global/en/news/magazine/2020/repurposin
g-natural-gas-infrastructure-for-hydrogen.html
[74]https://www.energynetworks.org/newsroom/hydrog
en-blending-what-is-it-and-why-does-it-
matter#:~:text=That%20trial%20has%20consisted%20of
,natural%20gas%20is%20well%2Destablished.
[75] https://hydeploy.co.uk/
[76]https://www.nrel.gov/news/program/2020/hyblend-

project-to-accelerate-potential-for-blending-hydrogen-in-natural-gas-pipelines.html

[77]https://www.energynetworks.org/newsroom/hydrogen-blending-what-is-it-and-why-does-it-matter

[78] https://youtu.be/DVYyajJYZQI

[79]https://www.aiche.org/chs/conferences/international-center-hydrogen-safety-conference/2019/proceeding/paper/review-hydrogen-tank-explosion-gangneung-south-korea

[80]https://www.engineeringtoolbox.com/ammonia-liquid-thermal-properties-d_1765.html

[81] https://www.nature.com/articles/d42473-020-00542-w

[82] https://pubchem.ncbi.nlm.nih.gov/compound/Toluene

[83] https://datasheets.scbt.com/sc-250391.pdf

[84]https://www.sciencedirect.com/science/article/abs/pii/S0360319918306967#:~:text=Ammonia%20borane%20is%20an%20appropriate,releasing%20hydrogen%20stored%20in%20it.

[85]https://www.chemistryworld.com/features/hydrogen-storage-gets-real/3010794.article#/?utm_source=spectra&utm_medium=referral

[86] https://www.bbc.co.uk/news/magazine-30405066

[87]https://www.uniper.energy/news/gie-press-release-european-underground-storages-keep-us-warm

[88]https://www.bgs.ac.uk/news/safe-storage-of-hydrogen-in-porous-rocks-the-challenges-and-knowledge-gaps/

[89]https://www.energy.gov/eere/fuelcells/site-and-bulk-hydrogen-storage

[90]https://www.beaumontenterprise.com/news/article/Air-Liquide-plans-subsurface-hydrogen-storage-10837245.php

[91]https://energies.airliquide.com/resources-planet-hydrogen/how-hydrogen-stored

[92]https://www.thechemicalengineer.com/features/hydrogen-the-burning-question/

[93]https://www.ge.com/power/gas/fuel-capability/hydrogen-fueled-gas-turbines

[94]https://www.ge.com/power/gas/fuel-capability/hydrogen-fueled-gas-turbines

[95]https://www.power-technology.com/comment/standing-at-the-precipice-of-the-hydrogen-economy/

[96]http://www.meca.org/technology/technology-details?id=5&name=Catalytic%20Converters

[97] https://afdc.energy.gov/fuels/hydrogen_basics.html

[98]https://ourworldindata.org/co2-emissions-from-transport

[99]https://interplex.com/resources/did-you-know/the-first-hydrogen-fuel-cell-vehicle-was-created-in-1966/#:~:text=The%20Electrovan%20from%20General%20Motors,liquid%20hydrogen%20and%20liquid%20oxygen.

[100]https://ourworldindata.org/co2-emissions-from-transport

[101]https://www.carsguide.com.au/car-advice/how-many-cars-are-there-in-the-world-70629

[102]https://www.statista.com/topics/1487/automotive-industry/

[103]https://fuelcellsworks.com/news/in-terms-of-

hydrogen-cars-south-korea-is-number-1-in-global-sales/

[104] https://ihsmarkit.com/research-analysis/ihs-markit-forecasts-global-ev-sales-to-rise-by-70-percent.html

[105]https://airqualitynews.com/2019/08/27/range-anxiety-still-biggest-ev-turn-off-survey-finds/

[106]https://fuelcellsworks.com/news/korea-first-hydrogen-refueling-station-in-sejong-city-completed/#:~:text=Currently%2C%20there%20are%2045%20hydrogen,charging%20stations%20nationwide%20by%202022.

[107]https://www.statista.com/statistics/1026088/south-korea-number-of-gas-stations-by-operator/

[108]https://www.reuters.com/article/us-autos-hydrogen-southkorea-insight-idUSKBN1W936A

[109]https://ourworldindata.org/co2-emissions-from-transport

[110]https://railway-news.com/hydrogen-is-a-distraction/#:~:text=Hydrogen%20trains%20are%20already%20in,And%20they%20have%20their%20place.&text='Green'%20hydrogen%20is%20made%20by,renewable%20energy%20and%20fuel%20cells.

[111]http://www.transport-network.co.uk/38-of-Britains-rail-network-now-electrified/16944

[112]https://economics.stackexchange.com/questions/19490/why-is-railway-electrification-in-north-america-far-less-common-than-in-europe

[113]https://www.railtech.com/rolling-stock/2019/12/11/bi-mode-trains-become-more-popular-in-uk/

[114]https://ourworldindata.org/co2-emissions-from-transport

[115]https://e360.yale.edu/features/at-last-the-shipping-industry-begins-cleaning-up-its-dirty-fuels

[116]https://www.heraldscotland.com/business_hq/18789 377.scotland-trial-worlds-first-hydrogen-powered-ferry-european-marine-energy-centre-orkney/

[117]https://www.euractiv.com/section/energy/news/den mark-and-norway-team-up-to-build-worlds-largest-hydrogen-ferry/

[118]https://ourworldindata.org/co2-emissions-from-transport

[119]https://www.theverge.com/2019/5/9/18538030/germa ny-ehighway-siemens-vw-group-electrified-cables-wires-overhead-electric-hybrid-trucks

[120] https://www.h2haul.eu/

[121]https://ourworldindata.org/co2-emissions-from-transport

[122]https://www.rechargenews.com/technology/worlds-first-hydrogen-powered-ferry-in-norway-to-run-on-green-gas-from-germany/2-1-976939

[123] https://youtu.be/WLKOsyMU-4o

[124]https://www.bbc.com/future/article/20201116-climate-change-how-to-cut-the-carbon-emissions-from-heating

[125]https://www.thegreenage.co.uk/comparing-the-us-and-the-uk-how-do-we-heat-our-homes/

[126] www.gov.uk/government/groups/heat-in-buildings

[127]https://www.theguardian.com/business/2021/feb/16/f irst-uk-homes-with-hydrogen-boilers-and-hobs-to-be-built-by-april

128
https://assets.publishing.service.gov.uk/government/u
ploads/system/uploads/attachment_data/file/760508/h
ydrogen-logistics.pdf

[129]https://ec.europa.eu/energy/content/space-heating-
heterogenous-among-european-
countries_en?redir=1#:~:text=There%20are%20about%2
0244%20million,are%20heated%20with%20collective%
20systems.

[130] https://www.hy4heat.info/wp2

[131]https://www.world-nuclear.org/our-
association/publications/online-reports/lifecycle-ghg-
emissions-of-electricity-
generation.aspx#:~:text=According%20to%20the%20Int
ergovernmental%20Panel,approximately%2037%25%2
0of%20global%20emissions.

[132]www.bp.com/content/dam/bp/business-
sites/en/global/corporate/pdfs/

[133]www.sciencedirect.com/science/article/abs/pii/S1385
89471731940X#:~:text=The%20reverse%20water%20gas
%20shift%20(RWGS)%20reaction%20is%20a%20metho
d,the%20conversion%20of%20CO2.

[134]www.netl.doe.gov/research/coal/energy-
systems/gasification/gasifipedia/ftsynthesis

[135]royalsociety.org/-/media/policy/projects/synthetic-
fuels/synthetic-fuels-briefing.pdf

[136]https://www.cleanenergywire.org/news/pilot-
project-germanys-largest-refinery-produce-synthetic-
fuels

[137]https://www.shell.com/business-
customers/aviation/the-future-of-energy/sustainable-

aviation-fuel/synthetic-kerosene.html

[138]https://www.google.com/search?q=global+cabon+foo
tprint+of+steel+production&rlz=1C1CHBF_en-
GBGB935GB935&oq=global+cabon+footprint+of+steel+
production&aqs=chrome..69i57j33i10i22i29i30.8019j1j4
&sourceid=chrome&ie=UTF-8

[139]techcrunch.com/2019/11/19/heliogens-new-
technology-could-unlock-renewable-energy-for-
industrial-manufacturing/

[140] heliogen.com/#how

[141]heliogen.com/time-names-heliogen-helioheat-to-list-
of-the-best-inventions-of-2020/

[142] https://www.h2greensteel.com/green-steel

[143] https://vimeo.com/544484332

[144]theconversation.com/green-ammonia-could-slash-
emissions-from-farming-and-power-ships-of-the-
future-132152

[145]www.economist.com/media/globalexecutive/black_s
wan_taleb_e.pdf

[146]www.health.ny.gov/environmental/emergency/chem
ical_terrorism/ammonia_general.htm

[147]www.royalsociety.org/topics-policy/projects/low-
carbon-energy-programme/green-ammonia/

[148]   https://www.intelligentliving.co/ammonia-fuel-of-
the-future/

[149]https://spectrum.ieee.org/transportation/marine/why
-the-shipping-industry-is-betting-big-on-ammonia

[150] https://www.chemengonline.com/acciona-launches-
worlds-first-blockchain-platform-for-tracking-and-
verifying-green-hydrogen/

[151] https://www.chemengonline.com/acciona-launches-

worlds-first-blockchain-platform-for-tracking-and-verifying-green-hydrogen/
[152]https://www.theguardian.com/environment/2019/aug/17/plastic-recycling-myth-what-really-happens-your-rubbish
[153]https://www.egginfo.co.uk/egg-facts-and-figures/industry-information/data
[154]https://www.theccc.org.uk/wp-content/uploads/2018/11/H2-report-draft-20181119-FINALV3.pdf
[155]https://www.shell.com/about-us/major-projects/sakhalin/sakhalin-an-overview.html
[156]https://www.woodside.com.au/what-we-do/australian-operations/north-west-shelf
[157]https://www.equinor.com/en/what-we-do/norwegian-continental-shelf-platforms/snohvit.html
[158] https://hynet.co.uk/

[159] www.jadecove.com/research/hydrogenscam
[160]https://www.spglobal.com/ratings/en/research/articles/210422-the-hydrogen-economy-for-light-vehicles-hydrogen-is-not-for-this-decade-11911374
[161]https://www.nextgreencar.com/electric-cars/statistics/
[162]https://www.theguardian.com/news/2017/dec/21/hinkley-point-c-dreadful-deal-behind-worlds-most-expensive-power-plant
[163] https://windeurope.org/about-wind/history/
[164]https://www.iea.org/reports/hydrogen-projects-database

[165]www.rechargenews.com/energy-transition/growing-ambition-the-worlds-22-largest-green-hydrogen-projects/2-1-933755

[166]https://www.idealhy.eu/index.php?page=lh2_outline#:~:text=Hydrogen%20is%20an%20excellent%20energy,www.h2data.de).

[167]https://energies.airliquide.com/resources-planet-hydrogen/how-hydrogen-stored

[168]www.ecowatch.com/coffees-invisible-carbon-footprint-1882175408.html#:~:text=Per%20cup%2C%20black%20coffee%20produces,%3B%20each%20latte%2C%20340%20grams.

[169]www.sixdegreesnews.org/archives/10261/the-carbon-footprint-of-a-cheeseburger

[170]publishing.rcseng.ac.uk/doi/pdf/10.1308/rcsbull.2020.152#:~:text=The%20carbon%20footprint%20result%20for,CO2e%20per%20hour%20of%20surgery.

[171] calculator.carbonfootprint.com/

[172] www.eurostar.com/be-en/carbon-footprint

[173]www.carbonbrief.org/analysis-uks-co2-emissions-have-fallen-29-per-cent-over-the-past-decade#:~:text=The%20UK's%20per%2Dcapita%20CO2,or%20the%20US%20(16.6).

[174]data.gov.uk/dataset/9a1e58e5-d1b6-457d-a414-335ca546d52c/provisional-uk-greenhouse-gas-emissions-national-statistics

[175]ourworldindata.org/co2-and-other-greenhouse-gas-emissions

[177]https://wedocs.unep.org/bitstream/handle/20.500.118

22/28246/7789GWPRef_EN.pdf?sequence=2&isAllowe
d=y

[178]https://assets.publishing.service.gov.uk/government/
uploads/system/uploads/attachment_data/file/760538/
Hydrogen_atmospheric_impact_report.pdf

[179] https://www.epa.gov/ghgemissions/understanding-
global-warming-
potentials#:~:text=Methane%20(CH4)%20is%20estimat
ed,uses%20a%20different%20value.).

[180]https://www.epa.gov/ghgemissions/understanding-
global-warming-
potentials#:~:text=Chlorofluorocarbons%20(CFCs)%2C
%20hydrofluorocarbons%20(,more%20heat%20than%2
0CO2.